PROFESSIONAL DEVELOPMENT FOR APPRAISAL AND REVALIDATION

THE DR HAIRY WORKBOOK

PROFESSIONAL DEVELOPMENT FOR APPRAISAL AND REVALIDATION

THE DR HAIRY WORKBOOK

DAVID HINDMARSH GP TRAINER IN KENT

& EDWARD PICOT PRACTICE MANAGER IN KENT

Scion

© **Edward Picot and David Hindmarsh**

ISBN 978 1 904842 97 2

First published in 2012 by Scion Publishing Ltd

A CIP catalogue record for this book is available from the British Library.

Scion Publishing Limited
The Old Hayloft, Vantage Business Park, Bloxham Road, Banbury,
Oxfordshire OX16 9UX, UK
www.scionpublishing.com

Important Note from the Publisher
The information contained within this book was obtained by Scion
Publishing Limited from sources believed by us to be reliable. However,
while every effort has been made to ensure its accuracy, no responsibility
for loss or injury whatsoever occasioned to any person acting or refraining
from action as a result of information contained herein can be accepted
by the authors or publishers.

Although every effort has been made to ensure that all owners of
copyright material have been acknowledged in this publication, we
would be pleased to acknowledge in subsequent reprints or editions any
omissions brought to our attention.

Readers should remember that medicine is a constantly evolving science
and while the authors and publishers have ensured that all dosages,
applications and practices are based on current indications, there may be
specific practices which differ between communities. You should always
follow the guidelines laid down by the manufacturers of specific products
and the relevant authorities in the country in which you are practising.

Typeset by Phoenix Photosetting, Chatham, Kent, UK
Printed by the Complete Product Company, Malmesbury, Wiltshire, UK

Books for the MRCGP

www.scionpublishing.com   www.facebook.com/medicbooksdirect

Cases and Concepts for the MRCGP 2e

Paperback

9781904842675

£26.99

★★★★☆ (2)

CSA Revision Notes for the MRCGP 2e

Paperback

9781907904073

£26.99

★★★★★ (9)

CSA Scenarios for the MRCGP 2e

Paperback

9781904842811

£27.99

★★★★★ (17)

Consultation Skills for the MRCGP 2e

Paperback

9781904842965

£27.99

★★★★☆ (11)

Applied Knowledge Test for the new MRCGP 2e

Paperback

9781904842767

£24.99

★★★★★ (3)

Books are available from all good booksellers.

Check out our Facebook page for the latest special offers on our medical books!

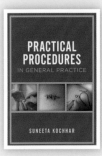

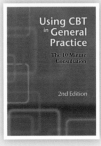

CONTENTS

CONTENTS

PREFACE

The origins of this book lie in another book which we produced in 2008 – *Dr Hairy's Guide to the GP Curriculum*. David Hindmarsh was then working as a Course Organizer, and he wanted to create a short and readable guide to the 600-page Curriculum which the RCGP had just published. The guide was written in plain language, with lots of examples and jokes.

Dr Hairy's Guide to the GP Curriculum didn't make us zillionaires, unfortunately, but it did sell enough copies to make us feel that there might be some mileage in our approach to medical education, and we soon started to think about another book.

Over several years David had collected lots of educational exercises (mainly to do with reflection and self-awareness) and tried them out on groups of Registrars; we wondered if a compilation of these might be of interest to other GPs. At the same time, Edward (who likes to fiddle around with bits of cheapish technology) had bought himself a video camera and some editing software, and was mulling over the possibilities of either making some training videos, or making some humorous short films about primary care, just for fun, using puppets instead of real people.

In the end we decided to combine all of these ideas.

We put together a small group of local GPs and started to hold monthly meetings after work. At these meetings we would show the latest Dr Hairy video, have a chat about it, then try out some of David's training exercises and have a chat about those too. It was all very informal, with snacks and drinks and lots of nattering, but from this rather loose process there gradually emerged both a sense of what we were trying to do and a method for doing it. This book is the result.

We would particularly like to thank the people who came to our meetings – especially Andrea Taylor, Peter Gildeh, Sheila Khehar and Selina Brewerton, who were our best attendees. We would also like to thank Martin Haley of GP Update, who was extremely generous with his time and advice while the book was being written.

David Hindmarsh and Edward Picot
December 2011

ABOUT THE AUTHORS

David Hindmarsh and Edward Picot have been working together in a surgery in Kent for more than twenty years. Before that they used to go to school together, sing in the choir together, and play each other at conkers.

David Hindmarsh is a GP Trainer, and he used to be a Course Organizer and a Child Protection Officer. Despite all his responsibilities, his extremely arduous working life and an inexplicable (but chronic) shortage of money, he is always cheerful and friendly and has never ever lost his temper, not even once. He attributes his extraordinary forbearance to the large numbers of biscuits he consumes every day.

Edward Picot is Dr Hindmarsh's practice manager, which in itself would be enough to drive most people right over the edge. Despite the increasingly Kafkaesque NHS bureaucracy within which he works, and the measly pittance which is all he gets for his efforts, he is always cheerful and friendly and has never ever lost his temper, not even once. He attributes his almost superhuman self-restraint to the large number of sarcastic remarks he makes every day, most of them aimed at Dr Hindmarsh.

If you'd like to get in touch with us about this book, we'd be delighted to hear from you. Please feel free to send us any comments and/or inquiries. Our email addresses are david.hindmarsh@nhs.net and edward@edwardpicot.com. We do have a very sophisticated spam filter, however, which will automatically block out anything unfavourable.

> Please note that the Dr Hairy videos on the DVD are provocative in nature and approach and the language is probably less formal than you might be used to (*OK, there's a bit of swearing, but nothing too rude ...*).
>
> This is deliberate:
>
> - we're not trying to shock you, but we do want to challenge you to think about the way you approach different types of situation
>
> - we also want to make you smile and enjoy the process – *and if you don't, it's obviously not our fault ...*

ABOUT THE BOOK

What's this book all about? What's the DVD for?

The DVD contains 13 videos about the travails and misadventures of an ordinary (but rather hirsute) GP called Dr Hairy.

The first 12 videos correspond with the 12 chapters in this book. (If you like, you could work through one a month to prepare for revalidation – but it's really up to you what pace you want to go at.) The 13th video (about Mentoring) is a kind of postscript.

There are also two extra videos, which relate to exercises in the book:

- Bramble jelly
- Everyone I can think of who has died

Is this meant to be serious, or is it meant to be funny?

Well, both. The humorous approach is part of a deliberate attempt to make our professional development training more

- fun
- unstuffy
- non-academic
- user-friendly
- down to earth, and
- a reflection of what it's really like to work in general practice.

We're hoping that when you see the videos, you'll (a) laugh at them, and (b) recognize some of the situations and themes in them. The questions and exercises in this book are then designed to take things a bit further by

- making you think a bit more deeply about the situations and themes in the videos

- helping you to think more widely about the context in which general practice takes place, and

- helping you to be more self-aware about where and how you fit into all this.

Who is this training meant to be for?

- Trainees

- GPs

- Trainers

- Programme directors

What do you mean by 'professional development'?

The exercises in this book, and the videos in the accompanying DVD, are designed to stimulate a creative approach to problems, and to get people thinking about the wider issues which form the context of general practice.

What does that mean? Well, let's suppose that a particular patient refuses to come for any chronic disease checks, never keeps any appointments with specialists at the hospital, and doesn't take her medication properly – but keeps calling out the ambulance or going to A&E in the middle of the night complaining of chest pains.

Or let's suppose that all the GPs in your surgery pass messages to each other or set up tasks for each other electronically, except for one, who insists on having all his results and correspondence on paper and all his tasks in handwriting.

There may not be any 'right' answers to problems like this. They can really get under your skin, and you can waste a lot of time grinding your teeth and pulling out your hair in big clumps as a result; but sometimes the best way to deal with them is to take a step back from the tangle, instead of trying to hack your way through the middle. Once you start to get some perspective you can sometimes see a way to circumvent the difficulty – or sometimes you can just see that actually it isn't such a big deal as you thought; it's quite commonplace in general practice, and you can live with it if you really have to.

How do you use the exercise book? And why's it got so much blank space in it? I paid good money for this book. I didn't expect it to be half-empty.

We've deliberately left plenty of blank space in every chapter, because you're supposed to get your pen out and write things down. Don't just read the questions; try to answer them. There are no right or wrong answers, but the process of putting something down on paper will really help you to formulate your ideas.

All right then, what are all these bloody poems in aid of? What's poetry got to do with being a GP?

We like poems, and they're terrific aids to reflection. The exercises in this book, along with the videos, have been road-tested with groups of registrars and GPs over the last two or three years. We were a bit hesitant at first when we started asking registrars and GPs to read and discuss poems, but the response has almost always been really positive.

Doctors are literate and well-educated people, and being a GP isn't just about science and technical know-how. There's a lot of interpretation and sensitivity to nuance involved as well. People who can respond well to a patient in a consultation can usually respond well to a poem.

Aids to reflection? What's reflection got to do with it? Why do you keep banging on about reflection?

There are already lots of factual and/or scientific training courses for GPs, but medicine – especially general practice – isn't just about facts and science. Think of it as a balance between the following:

Intuition	Analytical reasoning
Values and attitudes	Evidence
Feelings	Facts
Pattern recognition, experiential knowledge	Critical analysis

What links together the opposite sides of this table is reflection.

Reflection is about learning from experience. It can be thought of as a cycle, starting with a concrete experience which results in reflection and then the formation of ideas and concepts. These ideas are then tested out on a new situation (new experience) and the whole process starts again.

Here's one of those diagrams you always see in books like this:

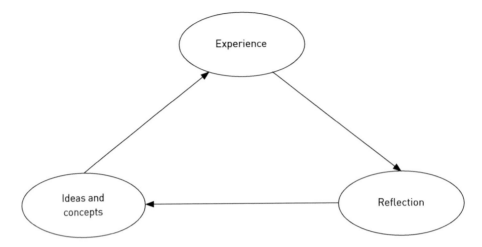

Or, to put it another way:

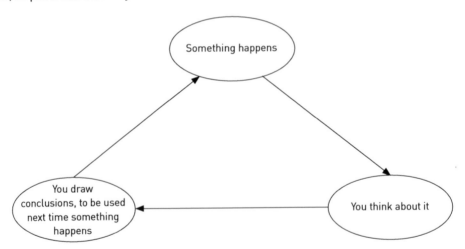

Donald Schön (an influential thinker about the theory and practice of reflective professional learning, and author of *The Reflective Practitioner* (1983) amongst other titles) talks about the hard ground and the swamp. The hard ground is where rules apply, e.g. therapeutic guidelines. In the swamp, on the other hand, there are no clear rules and we have to learn from reflection on experience. In general practice there are a lot of swamps.

The best GPs are not necessarily those with the widest and most detailed medical knowledge; and when things go wrong in general practice, although they can go wrong through medical errors, just as often they go wrong through failures of organization and lack of people skills.

You may have arranged all the correct diagnostic tests for a patient with suspected cancer, but if you lose the results or fail to act on them when they come through, then your clinical expertise isn't helping anybody.

Likewise, you can get by perfectly adequately as a GP without being able to name all the bones in the foot, providing you know where to lay your hands on the information if you need it. But you won't get by if you can't communicate with your patients, if you keep falling out with your colleagues, if you can't organize your time or if you can't cope with stress. Reflection, a sense of perspective and good self-awareness are vital in all these areas.

Here are the elements of reflective practice, which we have shamelessly adapted from a document called *Being a Reflective General Practitioner* which was produced by the East of England Multi-Professional Deanery in 2009:

- *Observation:* You are alert and observant and notice both what is obvious and less obvious about a situation. (The obvious might be: 'No wonder this patient's complaining of a headache – he's got a meat-cleaver in his head!' while the less obvious might be: 'Perhaps this indicates a stressful domestic environment.')

- *Self-awareness:* You are aware not only of what you think, but what you sense or feel about the experience. You are willing to take responsibility rather than put the responsibility on others (for example, when something goes wrong in a consultation you can recognize when it's your own fault, instead of always blaming somebody else).

- *Self-regulation:* You recognize when experiences and behaviour are outside what the profession would consider as being competent (for example, if you make a pass at an exceptionally attractive patient, or punch the nose of an exceptionally annoying one).

- *Internal conversation:* You try to make sense of your thoughts and feelings.

- *Openness:* You are open and honest about your own performance in relation to what might be expected by the profession.

- *Learning:* As a result of your reflections, you reach an understanding of what you need to learn and why you need to learn it.

Yeah, yeah, great. But how's all this going to help me with my revalidation?

Reflection is a very important concept in the revalidation process. Here are some quotes from the RCGP's *Guide to Revalidation for GPs* (Version 6, September 2011 – www.rcgp.org.uk/revalidation/revalidation_guide.aspx):

> It is very important that the GP **reflects** on the goal [of the Personal Development Plan], the development achieved and any reasons for not

achieving the goal. This **reflection** is an important attribute of a GP's fitness to practice.

Normally goals, whether met or not, should show supporting information of **reflection** on the personal development achieved and, if appropriate, the reasons for non-achievement.

The most important aspect of undertaking patient surveys is the **reflection** upon the results and, if appropriate, implementing changes.

[In assessing complaints made against a GP the assessor must] look for supporting information of the key attribute of **reflection** and improvement.

...for the purposes of revalidation each of the submitted [significant] events must demonstrate, through the analysis, areas for improvement, **reflection** and the implementation of change... the key attributes of a satisfactory Significant Event Audit are **reflection** and appropriate action undertaken.

...clinical audits are included in the standard portfolio to demonstrate that GPs set themselves appropriate criteria and standards; **reflect** on the care they deliver; and improve their care when necessary.

In fact the *Guide* as a whole makes it clear that the revalidation process will be looking for evidence, not just of training and learning, but of how GPs have developed their existing skills and working methods through 'reflection and appropriate change'.

This book can help you towards your appraisals and revalidation. If you do the exercises, you'll have lots of evidence of reflection to show to your appraiser. There are even videos about the appraisal process, and a mini-appraisal questionnaire for you to fill out.

Did I hear that there's another version of this book, designed to be used by groups instead of individuals?

That's right! As a matter of fact the videos and exercises in this book were originally road-tested with a small group of GPs, and some people may prefer to use our training in a group rather than in isolation. If you're interested in this approach, visit our website at http://drhairy.org.

CHAPTER **1**

VIDEO: ▶ Phoning the London Hospital

THEMES:

- Communication with other branches of the profession
- Using technology as a barrier instead of a facilitator
- Manipulative patients
- The frustration of dealing with large/impersonal organizations

QUESTIONS: ❓

Dr Hairy comes up against two of the ways in which telephone systems can drive their victims bonkers. The first is to leave them waiting in a queue for hours on end, whilst repeatedly telling them electronically that their call is important and playing them the same fragment of music. The second is to present them with one menu of options after another until they feel utterly bewildered and lost, then put them through to completely the wrong person or department.

What is the most irritating telephone system you've ever come up against yourself? Who did it belong to, and what was particularly annoying about it? What happened in the end? Did you get through, did you give up, did you make someone else ring them up instead, and when/if you finally got through did you make a complaint?

Thinking about your own surgery telephone system:

- When was the last time you tried ringing in from outside? If you haven't done it for a while, you might like to give it a try, and write down what you think about it afterwards.

- When you ring in, is the phone initially answered by a human being or an automated message?

- If it's an automated message, does it present you with any of the following?

  - A list of dos and don'ts – 'Don't order prescriptions over the telephone', 'Don't ring for results before 3 p.m.', etc.

  - A menu – 'Press 1 to make an appointment, Press 2 to ask for a result', etc.

  - A combination of the two.

- Do you think your telephone system compares well or badly with the telephone systems at other surgeries? And what impression do you think it gives callers?

Annoying though they can be, clearly these telephone systems are installed because people think they're a good idea. What's good about them? What benefits do they bring to the organizations that use them?

How many telephone lines do you have coming into your surgery? How many people do you have answering the phones at the busiest times of the week? Do they ever get rattled and crabby with people if things get really hectic? Could a more sophisticated telephone system help to reduce the stress?

If the best result for a patient calling the surgery is to get a real person picking up the telephone straight away, without any engaged signal, do you think this is achievable in terms of what your surgery can afford?

Now think about the wider issues. Technology can sometimes be very enabling for patients and surgery staff alike, but it can also sometimes shut people out or just confuse them. In other words it can be either user-friendly or user-unfriendly. In which category would you put the following?

- The Choose & Book system

- Your surgery website

- Online appointment-booking services

- Online prescription-ordering services

Add in any other examples of technology that come to mind. You can put things in both categories at the same time if you like.

User-friendly	User-unfriendly

EXERCISE: 🖊 Returning a faulty kettle

This exercise is about relationships between customers and shop staff – or it could equally well be patients and surgery staff.

Have you ever noticed that relationships between customers and shop-assistants are often very stressed-out and embattled? In an ideal world the customer goes into a shop to ask for something, the shop-assistant is courteous, friendly and helpful, and at the end of their interaction both of them feel satisfied with what has taken place. In the real world, shop-assistants are stressed-out and defensive, customers come into the shop with unreasonable demands, and a power-struggle ensues in which each party tries to get the better of the other. Pretty much the same thing happens in the NHS, between patients and reception staff, or between patients and their GPs (or between GPs and their reception staff, if we're honest).

Imagine a customer bringing back a faulty kettle to the electrical shop where it was bought, and trying to get a replacement or a refund for it. Below is a list of typical pushy-customer tactics, followed by a list of typical unhelpful-shop-assistant tactics. See how many you recognize from your own experience, either in shops or in the NHS.

Customer tactics:

- **I haven't got time for this.** I'm self-employed, and I've taken the morning off and driven over here today all the way from the other side of the county to bring this kettle back. I haven't got time to stand here and argue the toss. Time is money as far as I'm concerned. I've got a good mind to demand payment for my time as well as a refund for the price of the kettle.

- **Claiming expert knowledge.** My brother-in-law works in the factory that makes these kettles. He says no way should they break this quickly. He says they're required by European law to test them by boiling them when they're empty, and then running them over with a Ford Transit. He says if it's broken down this quickly then the maker's mark is probably a forgery and it's probably a cheap import, and I could probably sue you for selling it to me under false pretences.

- **Moral blackmail.** It's not for me, it's for my Mum. She's 87 years old, and she lives all by herself in a flat, and she can't afford to put the heating on. The only thing that keeps her going is making herself tea and Cup-a-Soups. She has trouble with solids these days. If she doesn't have a working kettle, she could easily die. You don't want her to die, do you?

- **I'm friends with your boss.** I played golf with him last week. He's a personal friend of mine. We're in the same lodge. He's coming round to mine for dinner on Friday. His children go to the same school as my children. You get him down here, and he'll soon sort this out. If he was here he'd just give me a new one, because he knows me.

- **Bullying.** You haven't heard the last of this. Either you give me a refund right now, or else I'm going straight out of here and I'm calling my solicitor. You've chosen the wrong person to be obstructive with this time, matey. What's your name? I'm writing it down, and I'm going to write an official letter of complaint. It's illegal to sell a dangerous kettle like that. I could have this shop closed. I could have this whole chain closed. Is that what you want? Is that what you want me to do?

- **You're the only one who can help me.** Oh, thank goodness it's you. I was hoping you'd be on duty. Everyone else that works here is useless, but I know you won't let me down. I just need to change this kettle for one that works properly – you don't mind me doing that, do you? I know you won't mind. You're always so friendly and helpful. Look, there's another one on the shelf. I'll just swap them over and nobody'll even notice.

Shop assistant tactics:

- **Pleading ignorance.** I'm sorry, but I'm new here, so I don't know what to do and I can't find out. Everybody else is at lunch. I don't know how to contact them. It's my first day. I've never even seen a kettle before.

- **Blaming a colleague.** Somebody else must have sold you that kettle. They never should have sold it to you. I never would have done it myself. A kettle like that's bound to go wrong. Didn't they tell you it's a bottom-of-the-range one? If you'd come in when I was on duty, I would have sold you something else instead. If you buy one like that, you're asking for trouble. I'm really surprised they didn't tell you.

- **Passing the buck.** You've got the wrong shop. We don't deal with that here. The shop which sells kettles is down the other end of the High Street. We used to sell kettles here, but we don't any more. But in any case you might need to send it back to Head Office by post. Or it might be the manufacturer that's responsible, not us at all – have you tried ringing them?

- **It's the system.** I'd like to help you, but I'm just as powerless as you are: it's the system: what can anybody do? They make these kettles badly on purpose. They don't want them to last. We're all in the same boat. I bought a kettle like that last week, and mine's broken too.

- **Blaming the complainant.** You must have done something wrong, otherwise there wouldn't be a problem. It's a perfectly good product. Are you sure you remembered to put some water in it before you switched it on? Or perhaps you put too much water in: they don't like that. Or perhaps the lid wasn't on properly.

- **Creating bureaucratic barriers.** Have you got the guarantee? The receipt? The original box? A photograph of yourself buying the kettle? Your passport? Your birth certificate? No? Well, I'm sorry, but if you look at the terms of sale on our website, it says quite clearly that no refunds will be given without the proper proof of purchase.

Go through the above lists. Put a tick against any tactics you've experienced in your own surgery. But an asterisk against any you have either used yourself, or had used on you by patients.

The point about this kind of tactical game is that the starting point of the conversation – the faulty kettle itself – soon becomes almost irrelevant, and the really important thing turns out to be a struggle for the upper hand between two (or more) individuals.

People who are really skilled at dealing with difficult members of the public – or at getting what they want out of stroppy shop assistants – can spot power-struggles like this developing and defuse them or steer round them. How do they do this? Good eye contact, good body language, sense of humour, empathy, good negotiating skills, offering small concessions in order to get big ones in return? Any other ideas?

POEM: 📖 Dirge of Dead Sisters

For the Nurses Who Died in the South African War

Who recalls the twilight and the ranged tents in order
   (Violet peaks uplifted through the crystal evening air?)
And the clink of iron teacups and the piteous, noble laughter,
   And the faces of the Sisters with the dust upon their hair?

(Now and not hereafter, while the breath is in our nostrils,
   Now and not hereafter, ere the meaner years go by –
Let us now remember many honourable women,
   Such as bade us turn again when we were like to die.)

Who recalls the morning and the thunder through the foothills,
   (Tufts of fleecy shrapnel strung along the empty plains?)
And the sun-scarred Red-Cross coaches creeping guarded to the culvert,
   And the faces of the Sisters looking gravely from the trains?

(When the days were torment and the nights were clouded terror,
   When the Powers of Darkness had dominion on our soul –
When we fled consuming through the Seven Hells of Fever,
   These put out their hands to us and healed and made us whole.)

Who recalls the midnight by the bridge's wrecked abutment,
   (Autumn rain that rattled like a Maxim on the tin?)
And the lightning-dazzled levels and the streaming, straining wagons,
   And the faces of the Sisters as they bore the wounded in?

(Till the pain was merciful and stunned us into silence –
   When each nerve cried out on God that made the misused clay;
When the Body triumphed and the last poor shame departed –
   These abode our agonies and wiped the sweat away.)

Who recalls the noontide and the funerals through the market,
   (Blanket-hidden bodies, flagless, followed by the flies?)
And the footsore firing-party, and the dust and stench and staleness,
   And the faces of the Sisters and the glory in their eyes?

(Bold behind the battle, in the open camp all-hallowed,
   Patient, wise, and mirthful in the ringed and reeking town,
These endured unresting till they rested from their labours –
   Little wasted bodies, ah, so light to lower down!)

Yet their graves are scattered and their names are clean forgotten,
   Earth shall not remember, but the Waiting Angel knows
Them who died at Uitvlugt when the plague was on the city –
   Her that fell at Simon's Town in service on our foes.

RUDYARD KIPLING

This poem is about Nurses in the Boer War in 1902, and the sacrifices they made in order to help the soldiers. Kipling implies that these sacrifices were made for religious reasons - hence 'the glory in their eyes', 'in the open camp all-hallowed' (hallowed meaning blessed or holy), and the reference to the Waiting Angel at the end of the poem.

He may also be implying that, although he clearly admires them, it's a shame to see such nice women throwing their lives away in a war. The description of their 'piteous, noble' laughter at the beginning of the poem, the reference to their 'little wasted bodies' (possibly 'wasted' in the sense of not having known love or borne children, as well as the more obvious meaning of 'wasted away'), and the fact that 'their names are clean forgotten' (which again may be a reference to the fact that they haven't perpetuated their names by having children) all seem to suggest this.

At the end of the poem, the line about 'Her that fell at Simon's Town in service on our foes' indicates that the sisters help both sides in the conflict. Kipling seems to be saying that the sisters are in the war without being part of it. There's something slightly incongruous about their angelic behaviour while everything around them is so brutal and hellish, and it almost seems as if their otherworldly calm is paid for by a willed detachment from the full horror of what is going on around them, and an indifference to the normal selfish pleasures of life, which mean that although they help other people to stay alive they are virtually throwing their own lives away, in order to obtain 'glory'.

This is a very different situation from general practice, but do you think it's the case that all medical practitioners have to find a way of coping with the brutalities of existence, and to some extent you're obliged to detach yourself and fix your mind on other things in order to do this?

Write your reactions to the poem on the next page.

CHAPTER 2

VIDEO: ▶ Private charges

THEMES:

- Private medicine vs. NHS medicine
- Charging (or not charging) for non-NHS services
- Bending the rules to curry favour with patients
- Patients falling victim to the intricacies of the system
- Relationships between different branches of medical practice

QUESTIONS: ❓

What's so good about private medicine? Why do some patients prefer it?

Why does Mrs Hattersley prefer private medicine in the video? Have you ever come across patients who prefer private medicine just because it's posher?

What's so good about private medicine from the practitioner's point of view? How nice is it to be completely in charge, instead of being told what to do by bureaucrats? Is the NHS going to be more like this once PCTs have been done away with?

Dr Goldfinger conspires with Mrs Hattersley to avoid her having to pay for her blood tests. He presents it as doing her a favour, but is he really just cheating the NHS? Is letting patients off charges one of the pleasures of private medicine, and one of the ways in which clinicians make themselves feel good by dispensing largesse to their patients?

On the other hand, how easy is it to adhere to Dr Wittgenstein's harder line? If Dr Goldfinger wrote to Dr Hairy, and asked Dr Hairy to arrange the blood tests, and Dr Hairy then sent copies of the results to Dr Goldfinger, it would all be on the NHS, wouldn't it? Is that right or wrong?

If a patient sees a private consultant and the private consultant recommends a cream, should the cream be prescribed privately or on the NHS? What about if it's a repeat prescription? Write down what you think the rules should be.

Answer at least one of the following:

Think of a patient from your surgery who never gets charged any private fees, or who you would never charge yourself. What are the reasons?

Do you tell patients about private charges yourself, or do you always get admin to do it? If you do it yourself, how do you approach the subject? If you get admin to do it, can you explain your reasons?

Write down your surgery rules/charges for

- Hepatitis B
- Prescriptions for patients going abroad for long periods
- Consultations with patients from overseas
- Medicines prescribed by private consultants
- Letters for patients about housing or benefits
- Copies from notes

(This might require a bit of homework)

Is Dr Wittgenstein's antagonism towards Dr Goldfinger an example of NHS antagonism towards private medicine, or an example of a biochemist's antagonism towards a gynaecologist, or both? Do both of them despise GPs?

Have you come across examples of people working in different departments or specialisms in the health sector finding fault with each other and despising each other from a safe distance? If you have, write a short description below. If you haven't, you've clearly just arrived here from a different planet.

EXERCISE: ✏ Good clinic / bad clinic

Write two lists, one of all the things a patient would expect to find in the perfect clinic, and one of all the things a patient would expect to find in a not-very-nice clinic. For example:

- up-to-date magazines
- out-of-date posters
- fluff under the chairs
- a well-kept garden
- nice curtains
- music in the waiting room
- staff in uniform
- electronic sign-in facilities
- potted plants
- a water cooler
- noise
- stressed-out receptionists
- snooty receptionists

Good clinic	Bad clinic

Now go back to the lists.

- Mark a P against each item you would tend to associate with a private clinic.
- Mark an N against each item you would tend to associate with an NHS clinic. (Items can be marked both P and N)
- Mark an S against each item you recognize from your own surgery.

If you were given £1000 to spend on improving the look/ambience/customer experience in your own surgery, what would you spend it on?

How important do you think layout, decoration, cleanliness, etc. are to the patient experience, and/or to the working experience of staff?

EXERCISE: ✎ Leadership styles

Leadership is about getting from where we are now to where we want to be. The Darzi Report placed a lot of emphasis on leadership; leadership now features in all the medical curricula, and GP Consortia are expected to show leadership in reorganizing the NHS and cutting costs.

Here are some different models of leadership

- **Transformational leadership** – about encouraging people to reach their full potential, e.g. getting the practice nurse to take responsibility for diabetic checks, or asking a registrar to give a presentation at the practice meeting about identifying carers. One problem with this can be that people start to think they're now too important to do the routine stuff, like emptying the dressings-bin when it's full or putting the otoscope back where it came from.

- **Distributed leadership** – working as a unit with different people taking the lead when appropriate. Can be an excuse for people to say things like 'Well, that's not my problem – Brenda looks after the photocopier'. Alternatively, it can result in everybody arguing with everybody else.

- **Charismatic leadership** – getting people to follow you and do as you ask by persuading them that you're a special person, a visionary or a hero – e.g. Jesus, Napoleon, Hitler, Churchill, Gandhi.

- **Transactional leadership** – carrot and stick. 'Do as I say and you get a reward; don't do as I say and you get a punishment'. It works with children and dogs. The trouble is, you have to do all the thinking, and the children and dogs don't get much chance to make a contribution (which is also a problem with the Charismatic model).

Which of these models are you most familiar with from working in the NHS? Can you give an example? Do you think the same things could have been accomplished using one of the other leadership methods?

Of the leadership models above, which do you think would be most appropriate to the following tasks:

- Making sure that clinical letters are always delivered to the surgery within a working week of the patient being seen at the hospital

- Persuading GPs, in order to save money, that they should reduce their referral rates

- Getting GPs and other surgery staff actively involved in consortia, and encouraging them to come up with innovative ideas

- Making sure that nobody ever shares a smartcard, or leaves it on the desk or in the slot of their computer overnight

- Persuading GPs in your surgery to change their working hours to suit the needs of their patients (e.g. opening on a Saturday or in the evenings)

- Organizing the changeover to a new clinical computer system

Consider your experiences of being led and your own experiences of being a leader.

- What do you think are the features of a good leader?

- Have you had experience of bad leadership? What was bad about it?

Can we all be leaders? Answer at least one of the following:

- People take on different roles in groups. In order for a group to function well, does there have to be a blend of leaders and other roles? If so, what are the other roles?

- Does power limit the ability of the less powerful to show leadership? In other words, once particular group members are perceived to have authority, does this discourage anyone else from exhibiting leadership?

- Does everyone in the group have to have the same level of understanding and knowledge – if not, are the ideas of the less knowledgeable group members likely to be discounted as less valid, and is this fair?

CHAPTER **3**

VIDEO: ▶ Old-fashioned medicine

THEMES:

- Professional etiquette between medical practitioners

- Preventive/box-ticking medicine vs. 'old fashioned' symptom-driven medicine

- Bullying in the workplace

- Patients who kid themselves about their weight (or other areas of health)

- Why are appetites so difficult to control (smoking, drinking, gambling and sexual appetite as well as overeating)? Why do we do things when we know they're bad for us?

- 'I don't want to get old and die' as against 'Are you going to enjoy your life while you've got it?'

QUESTIONS: ❓

Dr Hairy has given Mr Fapso advice about trying to lose weight and take more exercise. When Mr Fapso reports back he is seen by Dr Gladstone, who tells him something completely different.

What are the professional ethics of this situation? Have you ever had your advice to a patient contradicted by another doctor?

Think of an example where you have taken over the care of a patient from a colleague, and felt that the colleague was handling the case differently from the way you would prefer. What did you do? How did the patient react? How did the colleague react when he/she found out, or didn't that happen?

If the general rule is not to contradict what your colleagues have said, what are the circumstances in which this rule needs to be broken?

Dr Gladstone is an 'old-fashioned' GP who thinks patients should come and see him when they've actually got something wrong with them, and regards preventive medicine as a waste of time. He doesn't like the 'box-ticking' approach because it diminishes his autonomy as a practitioner and erodes the individuality of the patient.

Where do you stand on this issue? How do you feel about the QOF points system and its effects?

Is this a generational thing – are all doctors over the age of sixty suspicious of preventive medicine and 'box-ticking', whereas doctors under the age of forty take it for granted as part of modern general practice? Can you think of any examples which contradict this cliché?

Dr Gladstone prides himself in knowing the patients personally. Do you think the trend in general practice is away from personal relationships with the patients, and towards a more methodical, impersonal approach – and is this a good thing or a bad thing?

Mr Fapso is very evasive and defensive about his own weight – and in fact he has managed to completely kid himself that he can't be overweight, when it's obvious to Dr Hairy that he really is.

What's the most bizarre excuse you've ever heard from a patient for their apparent weight gain? (e.g. 'It's really my jumper', 'I absorb fat from the atmosphere because I work in a chip shop', 'I've got heavy bones') How did you deal with it?

Dr Gladstone is even fatter than Mr Fapso – but at least he doesn't try to adopt a 'holier-than-thou' attitude about his weight. You probably know of GPs who are overweight, drinkers, smokers, drug-takers, etc. How do these GPs handle the task of telling their patients to lose weight, cut down on the booze or lay off the fags? Do their own weaknesses put them at an obvious disadvantage, or do they somehow manage to make them count in their favour?

When Dr Hairy was a registrar he was evidently bullied and taken advantage of by Dr Gladstone.

Have you come across any examples of senior GPs bullying and/or exploiting their junior colleagues in this way?

Sometimes even senior receptionists, admin staff or practice nurses can intimidate junior doctors – have you come across examples of this?

On the other hand, working with colleagues from different generations can sometimes be a very positive experience. Can you think of an example of something you have learnt from a considerably older or considerably younger colleague, which has really helped you in your work? Do you think that being older or being younger gave the colleague a different perspective from your own?

Answer one of the following:

- If you haven't weighed yourself for more than a year, do so. You don't have to specify the results, but write an account of the reasons why you weren't weighing yourself, and your feelings about stepping onto the scales.

- Which would you rather do, live a long but dull and frustrating life, or live a short but very fulfilled one? If possible, give examples of people whose lives fit one or the other of those descriptions.

EXERCISE: ✎ The consultation journey

Dr Hairy and Dr Gladstone have rather different consultation techniques. Below is a checklist of stages that may occur on the consultation journey (this is largely based on Roger Neighbour's book, *The Inner Consultation: how to develop an effective and intuitive consulting style*, 2nd ed, Radcliffe Medical Press, 2004).

Do you think all these stages occur in every consultation, or some in one and some in another? Are there any you use all the time and find particularly effective? Are there any you never use?

- *Opening gambit/ice-breaker:* One of these is the first thing the patient says when he or she walks into the room, e.g. 'I've had a very long wait, Doctor. What's the point in having appointment times and then not sticking to them?' Another is the first thing the patient says about the reason he or she has come to see you, e.g. 'I think I must have had a dodgy Chinese on Saturday because I've had constant diarrhoea ever since.'

- *The patient goes first:* Let the patients have their say, find out what they are thinking, let them get things off their chest.

- *Listen:* Don't just sit there staring out of the window. Make some eye contact, raise your eyebrows, lean forward, make encouraging noises, and don't interrupt too soon.

- *Empathy:* Try to put yourself in the patient's shoes.

- *Sign-posting:* 'I'll listen to your chest and take your blood pressure in a moment, but first tell me a bit more about the pain in your hip.' This reassures the patient that you are not ignoring their concerns but need to do things in a certain order.

- *Explain why you asked:* 'The reason I asked you about flashing lights and disorientation is that they can both be symptoms of migraine. Or aliens landing in your garden.'

- *ICE:* Ideas, concerns and expectations – what the patient thinks, or is concerned about, or expects you to do. They may not always be clearly stated, so you have to try to spot them as they arise. Patients who say 'I'm not worried about it, Doctor, it's not bothering me at all, I just thought I ought to mention it' are often going to go home to their partners and say, 'They never even sent me for a bloody scan, even though it's obvious that I'm really worried about cancer!' – so you have to be able to read between the lines.

- *Context:* Social, psychological, physical – consider all these factors and their relevance to the patient's problems. For example, a patient suffers from severe headaches when he wakes up every morning. On investigation it turns out he gets blind drunk with the lads every night (social) because he's under terrible stress at work (psychological), and when he gets home his wife always bangs him over the head with a frying pan (physical).

- *Summarize:* Check with the patient that you have understood the story correctly. 'So your *wife* turned out to be a *bloke*?!'

- *My friend John:* 'I had another patient with a similar problem to yours, and he was really concerned about...' This can be useful if you suspect that your patients have problems they are embarrassed to talk about.

- *Internal search:* If you ask the patient something and they feel a bit uncertain how much they trust you or how much they want to share with you, they may do an 'internal search' where they become quiet and look down or from side to side while they are thinking. The key here is not to interrupt. (On the other hand, if the reason for this behaviour is that a button has just popped off the patient's shirt and he's looking around for it, you could offer to help.)

- *Stepwise explanation:* 'You know that you've been on tablets for high blood pressure for a long time. Well, high blood pressure increases the risk of furring up or narrowing of the blood vessels, like the blood vessels in your leg for example. If the blood vessels in your leg get narrow, then when you walk uphill and your leg muscles need more blood, the blood may struggle to get through, and that may be why you are getting pains in your calf...'

- *Gift wrapping:* When you are offering the patient management options you may 'dress up' the one that seems best for that patient. 'Well, we could start you on a statin, or you could try to control your cholesterol through diet. Of course if you did manage to control it through diet then you'd probably feel a lot healthier as a result, and you'd also be costing the NHS less...' (N.B. This never works.)

- *Handover:* Sharing management plan and options. Checking understanding and agreement. 'OK, so you're going to take one of these tablets every day for a month, then come back and see me and I'll check your blood pressure again.'

- *Safety-netting:* 'OK, so you're going to take one of these tablets every day for a month, but if your skin turns blue or your fingernails fall off then stop taking them and come back straight away.'

- *Housekeeping:* Measures to ensure that you stay in good shape for the next consultation. Wash your hands, take a sip of your cold coffee, check the cricket score on the internet, blow your nose and look at the contents of your hanky, then call the next patient.

Neighbour suggests that you could keep a set of cards on your desk, with the name of a different consultation stage written on each card; then pick one at random and try to use that skill or spot that stage in the next consultation.

Another good idea is to record all instances of one particular stage – for example, record all the ice-breakers/opening gambits you get on a particular day. Try to work out what they mean. For example, if a patient comes into a consultation and says 'Don't ask me how I'm feeling!' as an opening gambit, what does this mean and how does it set the tone for the rest of the consultation?

Alternatively, you could score your consultations on a grid (*see below*) to develop insight into your own consulting patterns. This is quite difficult to do while the consultation is in progress, so you can either try to remember the detail of the consultation just after it finishes, or make some videos and 'mark' them afterwards (which is a particularly good exercise for registrars).

Neighbour's consultation stages (scoresheet)

	Opening gambit	Patient goes first	Listen	Empathy	Sign-posting	Explain why you asked	ICE	Context	Summarize	My friend John	Internal search	Stepwise explanation	Gift wrapping	Handover	Safety-netting	Housekeeping
Patient 1																
Patient 2																
Patient 3																
Patient 4																
Patient 5																
Patient 6																
Patient 7																
Patient 8																
Patient 9																
Patient 10																
Patient 11																
Patient 12																

EXERCISE: ✒ 'Everything worth doing is either illegal, immoral or fattening'

In the video, Mr Fapso says he doesn't want to get old and die. Dr Gladstone says the real question is whether he's going to enjoy his life while he's still got it.

Here is a list of activities:

Arguing

Cooking

Shopping

Making love

Playing games

Drinking alcohol

Smoking tobacco

Hosting a dinner party

Redecorating the house

Making someone feel guilty

Attending someone else's dinner party

Reading professional development books

Reading medical textbooks

Feeling guilty yourself

Paying your taxes

Driving your car

Raising children

Going to work

Having a poo

Dancing

Running

Eating

See if you can place these activities on the following grid:

Fun, and good for you	Fun, but bad for you
No fun, but good for you	**No fun, and bad for you**

Items from the list may fit into more than one category. Why do people ever do things which are no fun and bad for them? Do you have to have elements from all these categories to get a good work–life balance?

CHAPTER 4

VIDEO: ▶ Dr Hairy's address to the nation

THEMES:

- Does technology help us, or does it hinder us?
- Patients who cope with unhappiness by overeating (gala pork pies)
- The work–life balance
- Do something interesting with your life
- Value systems: the dog vs. the £5 note: if money and looks aren't the only things that matter, what else is there?

QUESTIONS ❓:

Dr Hairy mentions how long it takes him to get through his e-mails every day. How much time per day or week do you think you spend on your own e-mails?

What's your routine for dealing with them? Do you look at them once a week, once a day, or keep looking all the time? Do you go right through them from one end to the other, or do you just 'cherry-pick'?

Do you ever send e-mails to people who work in the same surgery, instead of talking to them, and if so, why?

What's your level of technical competence with e-mail? How many of the following things do you know how to do? (Mark the list with ticks or crosses.)

- Open an e-mail attachment

- Save an e-mail attachment elsewhere if you want to keep it

- Make an attachment (e.g. a picture or a Word document) to an e-mail of your own

- Forward an e-mail to somebody else

- Send an e-mail to one person, with a copy to another person

- Create a distribution list (e.g. for emails to every member of your surgery team)

- Create a rule so that all emails from a particular address (the college, perhaps) are filtered off to a separate folder.

Dr Hairy mentions a list of the kind of people society used to admire 'in the old days': Shakespeare, Elizabeth Fry, Gandhi and Pelé. He goes on to fulminate in a curmudgeonly way about the modern cult of celebrity.

Think of one celebrity you would like to be, and one person (famous or otherwise) who has been an important role model in your life, and give the reasons for your choice in each case.

Alternatively, answer this question:

Confess! Do you ever watch

- *The X Factor*
- *Britain's Got Talent*
- *I'm a Celebrity, Get me Out of Here*
- *The Apprentice*

- and if so, what do you think of them?

Dr Hairy seems to think that although people tend to live longer nowadays, the quality of their lives isn't necessarily improving – in fact he associates living longer with alcoholism, obesity and depression. Would you agree with this observation from your own experience, and how much of a problem do you think it is for the NHS?

Dr Hairy also remarks that his dog doesn't need any money to enjoy itself. Of course Dr Hairy has to earn the money to pay for his dog's food, but all the same dogs do seem to be able to 'live in the moment' and have spontaneous fun more easily than human beings.

- Have you got any pets?
- If you could be any animal, which one would you be?
- What kind of fun do you like to have that doesn't cost anything? (Try not to be too sexually explicit.)

Answer at least one of the following questions:

- Imagine you were in charge of the world for a day and you were allowed to change just one thing. What would it be, and why?

- Imagine you were in charge of the world for a day and you were allowed to have just one category of people lined up against a wall and shot. (If you're soft-hearted you can just have them abolished.) Who would it be, and why?

- Imagine you won £25 million in the National Lottery (you must have played this game in your head already.) What would you do with the money? Would you carry on working? Where would you like to live?

- Imagine if you hadn't become a GP – what do you think you might have become instead? What were the other subjects you were good at when you were at school, and what do you think they might have led to? Is any of this reflected in what you do with your private time when you're not at work?

- Dr Hairy's last word of advice is that you should do something interesting with your life. Do you think you're doing something interesting, just by being a GP? If not, what else are you doing, or what else would you like to do if you could?

EXERCISE: ✏ EBM and VBM

EBM is evidence-based medicine and VBM is values-based medicine. Which category do the following fit into? (Items can be placed in both categories if you like.) After you've been through the list, think about which of the two sides you find yourself leaning towards. If you've been in practice more than five years, do you think your answer now is different from what it would have been five years ago, and if so, which direction do you seem to be travelling in?

EBM		VBM
	Science	
	Art	
	Prescribe	
	Attitudes	
	Certainty	
	Feelings	
	Profit	
	Empiricism	
	Culture	
	Positivism	
	Beliefs	
	Doctor-centred	
	Patient-centred	
	Protocols	
	Reassure	
	Guidelines	
	Uncertainty	
	Disease process	
	Communication	
	Professionalism	
	Self-awareness	
	QOF	
	Targets	
	Compassion	
	Quantitative research	
	Qualitative research	
	Chronic disease management	
	Appraisal	
	Possibilities	
	Probabilities	
	Objective	
	Holistic	
	Cause and effect	
	Subjective	
	Dissection	
	Intuition	

EXERCISE: ✎ Five a day

This exercise is borrowed from a website called 'mindapples' at http://mindapples. org/. Write down in the table below what five things you do (or think it would be good to do) every day (or regularly) to keep yourself in good mental shape.

Try to generalize your suggestions as much as possible: for example, if one of your answers is 'Go for a walk', but you might also get similar benefits from a jog or a cycle ride, then a more general answer would be 'Therapeutic exercise'. But don't force the issue: if you really think there's something good about a walk which you can't get from any other form of exercise, that's OK.

1.	
2.	
3.	
4.	
5.	

Now let's imagine you've had a bad day at the surgery. Everything's gone wrong, everybody got cross with everybody else, and you're not sure you've made the right decisions. Three possible ways of dealing with this after you get home are:

- **Relieving the tension:** Finding some good way to let off steam (e.g. shouting at the kids, kicking the dog, chopping wood, tossing the caber)

- **Escapism:** Finding something completely different to think about, to take your mind off your troubles (e.g. going to a concert, playing chess, putting up a shelf)

- **Analysis:** Finding some way to go through your thoughts and feelings really thoroughly, until you've sorted them out to your own satisfaction (e.g. writing everything down in your diary, talking things over in detail with a close friend, or confiding in a whisper to your teddy bear at bedtime)

Which of these categories do your 'five a day' exercises fit into?

EXERCISE: 🖊 Creative thinking

Much of the material in this section is based on the writings of Edward de Bono (www.edwarddebono.com). De Bono is an authority 'in the field of creative thinking and the direct teaching of thinking as a skill', and he is also 'the originator of lateral thinking'. He has developed mental exercises and tools which allow people to deal with problems more effectively by thinking 'outside the box' about them.

Why are children more creative than adults?

De Bono's theory is that combinations of experiences and concepts build up patterns in our brains. These patterns may constrain our thought processes. In order to be more open-minded, we need to be able to think laterally, like children who have not formed rigid patterns yet.

The three ages of man:

- 0–5 years old: the age of Why? – collecting information

- 5–10 years old: the age of Why Not? – new ways of looking at the world

- 10–75 years+: the age of Because – established views.

Art and humour may be useful in opening up new channels for thought and new ways of seeing, as they often link things that may not appear to be linked logically.

The brain as a processing system

Imagine the brain as a jelly and experiences as hot ink being dropped into the jelly. If new experiences are dropped into the jelly close to each other, they may run into each other, forming patterns and channels. The patterns are very useful because they mean that we don't have to constantly relearn everything from scratch; but they also lead us to act or think in pre-set and predictable ways. When new ink is dropped into the jelly, it becomes more and more likely to flow along one of the existing channels, instead of creating a fresh one. Eventually almost all experiences tend to flow into pre-existing channels, and it becomes very difficult for the mind to cope with new experience or think beyond its accustomed patterns.

First stage and second stage thinking

First stage thinking is at the perception level. Second stage thinking is after perception and based on our assumptions and fixed way of looking at things – our 'concept package'.

First stage thinking: 'Stuff coming down from the sky.' Second stage thinking: 'It's raining. If I go out in this, I'll get wet.'

If we can consider that the obvious way of seeing is not the only way, then we do not take perception for granted. Creative thinking takes us back to the perception stage and can offer a way out of the fixed concept package – it deals with new ways of seeing and can lead to change and improvement.

Beyond Yes and No: 'Po'

No is the basic tool of the logic system – 'No, we couldn't solve all our problems by just giving everyone in the country £1 million each. The country couldn't afford it, and it would create rampant inflation.'

Yes is the basic tool of the belief system – 'Yes, if we pay our debts and live within our means, then things are bound to get better in the long run.'

'Po' is the basic tool of the creative system. It is a method of approaching problems in a new and creative way. 'We're short of hospitals and we don't know what to do with all our waste paper. Why don't we build hospitals out of waste paper?' This kind of 'blue sky' thinking or 'thinking outside the envelope' may sometimes produce frivolous or nonsensical ideas (although obviously not in the preceding example) but it can also get beyond the sense of being 'stuck' or 'bogged down' and create real breakthroughs.

Intermediate impossible and random juxtaposition

Think of an idea which is wrong or impossible. For example, 'All decisions about the NHS should be made by an ant' or 'GPs would be better at their jobs if they were forced to get drunk before they came to work'. Now try to write a list of ways in which there might actually be something of value in the idea.

Now pick a subject you'd like to discuss – for example, chronic kidney disease. Then pick a word at random from the dictionary, e.g. 'elephant'. Now try to think of relationships or connections between the two. It's actually very difficult to find a random word which can't be connected to a given subject in one way or another.

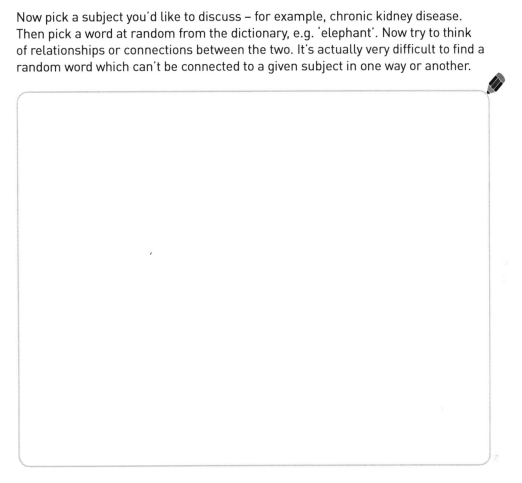

Now write a science fiction novel in which the NHS has been taken over by a giant ant, all the GPs are drunk, and teams of elephants are taking care of the CKD patients.

CHAPTER 5

VIDEO: ▶ Frank talking (Part 1)

THEMES:

- Consultation techniques
- How to deal with an irritating patient
- Absurd/unreasonable requests from patients
- Patients with their own agendas

QUESTIONS ❓:

Mrs Hattersley is convinced that her detached scab is medically significant and ought to be sent off somewhere for analysis. She also has her own agenda: she has kept all her scabs in a scab collection, and she wants Dr Hairy to find a home for the collection at a posh research hospital, because she wants to outdo her friend Mrs Prolapse who's keeping a toenail collection. Later on, she wants Dr Hairy to help her out with a query about her cat, because it would be too expensive for her to go to a vet.

Have you come across examples of patients who brought their own agendas or inappropriate requests to the consultation, and how did you deal with them?

How do you make patients stick to relevant subjects? Do you have any phrases you use to bring them back to the point? Examples might include 'Just coming back to the question of...' or 'Before we move on to that, let's just finish talking about...', or even 'I think we're drifting off the point...'

In order to get Dr Hairy to comply with her requests, Mrs Hattersley uses three tactics:

- She keeps telling him how nice he is

- She keeps telling him she's sure he must have more important things to worry about than a silly old thing like her – which is a way of hinting that he can't be bothered with her because of her age

- She occasionally refers to mistakes he has made in her care in the past, and uses them to blackmail him

Think of your most manipulative patients. Do they use the same methods as Mrs Hattersley, or different ones?

Dr Underslider, when he hears that a particular patient has been driving Dr Hairy to distraction, thinks it might be a poncy London barrister; but then agrees that old ladies can be even worse. Below is a list of some of the most irritating types of patient. Write numbers next to them, to rate them in order of irritatingness.

Teachers	
Old people who never listen to a word you're saying, and won't stop talking themselves	
Over-protective parents consulting about their children (especially if the children are old enough to come by themselves)	
Poncy London barristers, who think they're too important to have to comply with normal surgery procedures	
Patients with a bit of medical knowledge of their own, who insist on trying to show you how clever they are – for example ex-nurses, homeopaths, cranial osteopaths, radiology technicians	
A grown-up child who only visits his / her parent once every few months, but who then immediately rings the surgery to complain about the parent's state of health and insist that it needs sorting out straight away	
People who insist on being seen on an urgent basis when they've only got sore throats or earaches	
People who genuinely think they're dying when they've only got sore throats or earaches	
People who turn up with a cutting from the *Daily Mail* about some new wonder drug which has just been trialled in the USA, and want to know why they can't have a prescription for it right here and right now	
Any suggestions of your own?	

Dr Hairy's second consultation with Mrs Hattersley is really all about the gap between what he would like to say to her and what he feels allowed to say within the bounds of politeness.

Can you think of an example of a GP who is brutally honest with patients? How effective does this seem to be as a working method?

Conversely, can you think of a GP who is always charming and helpful, even when the patients are being unreasonable? What do you think of this as a working method?

Do doctors end up self-selecting the patients they deserve? For example, do brutally honest doctors end up with a list of patients who like no-frills treatment – 'just give me the antibiotics and never ask me about my mental state' – while 'softy' doctors end up with a list of blubbering fuss-pots? Where would you put yourself on this scale – do you wish you could be tougher and straighter-talking, or do you sometimes think you ought to be a bit more sympathetic and patient?

Going back to the question of making patients stick to relevant subjects – people may sometimes seem to be rambling on about nothing in particular, but then there comes a moment when they 'break through' to the real crux of what is bothering them. Can you think of an example where this has happened in your own experience? Did it fundamentally alter your view of the patient concerned? And did you actually do anything about the material which came to the surface in this 'breakthrough', or did you feel that it was enough just to have listened?

EXERCISE: ✏ Red flag game

This is partly a test of your knowledge base, partly about patient safety and partly about your insight into patients' ideas and concerns. Simply look at the presenting complaint and try to work out:

*   what is the worst possible diagnosis or diagnoses?

*   what is the most likely diagnosis or diagnoses?

*   what might the patient think is wrong?

*   what are the red flag signs or symptoms and what examination is essential?

You might also like to write on this page the most bizarre example you've ever come across of a patient misinterpreting his or her own symptoms.

Red flag game

Presenting complaint	Worst (likely) diagnosis	Most likely diagnosis
Back pain		
Abdominal pain (20 year old female, RIF pain)		
Dyspepsia, epigastric pain		
Night sweats		
Headache		
Rash		
Chest pain		
Bloated abdomen		
Febrile child		
Constipation		
Inconsolably crying baby		
'Funny turn'		

What might the patient think	Red flag symptoms/signs – essential examination

Red flag game (cont'd)

Presenting complaint	Worst (likely) diagnosis	Most likely diagnosis
Dyspnoea in young man		
Dyspnoea in middle-aged patient		
Visual disturbance, blurring		
Eye pain		
Tinnitus or hearing loss		
Vertigo		
Tingling or numbness		
Limb pain		
Painful joint, child		
Painful joint, adult		
Vomiting		
Hiccups		

What might the patient think	Red flag symptoms / signs – essential examination

EXERCISE: ✏ Heron's six interventions

Heron identified six interventions which may be used in a consultation (John Heron, *Six-Category Intervention Analysis*, 3rd ed, University of Surrey, 1989):

- Prescriptive – be bossy, tell them what to do

- Informative – tell them about something, explain

- Supportive – be comforting, approving, affirming (careful not to collude)

- Confronting – talk frankly, identify a problem or behavioural issue (within a caring context)

- Cathartic – make them cry or laugh, a release of emotions

- Catalytic – encourage self-exploration (increase the rate of a reaction – 'come on, hurry up')

Keep a chart of how/if you use these interventions in your own consultations over a period of a week or two (*see below*).

For each consecutive consultation in a surgery session, record the intervention used by putting a tick in the appropriate box. It is possible that you may use more than one intervention in a consultation – that's fine, just record each intervention. Make a brief note of the context of the consultation, e.g. bereavement, sore throat, etc. Finally, record whether you felt that the outcome was positive or negative (put a plus or a minus in the final column).

After recording the interventions used in a few surgery sessions, add up how often you use each intervention (and, if you're feeling particularly nerdy, make a bar chart). This will give you some insight into the interventions you use most or least commonly.

Look at the context of the consultations and see what the link is between context and intervention used – do you think you used the right intervention for the context?

Finally, look at the perceived outcome for each intervention – do some interventions have more positive or negative results than others?

Heron's six interventions (scoresheet)

Patient	Context (e.g. depression)	The interventions (*tick as appropriate*)						Outcome (+/–)
		Prescriptive	Informative	Supportive	Confronting	Cathartic	Catalytic	
1								
2								
3								
4								
5								
6								
7								
8								
9								
10								
11								
12								

CHAPTER **6**

VIDEO: ▶ **Frank talking** (Part 2)

THEMES:

- Sexual relationships/harassment in the workplace

- Sexual relationships/harassment with patients

- Ways of dealing with impossible patients (Dr Underslider's button-pressing scam)

- How much do GPs rely on their administrators and other staff? (How helpless is Dr Hairy when Tina leaves? Should he really try to learn how the photocopier works?)

- Does straight talking always fail or is it sometimes necessary and useful?

- Which should take priority, your personal relationship with someone you work with, or your formal relationship? How do you find a balance?

- Patient complaints

- How to cope in times of stress

QUESTIONS ❓:

All GPs should be well-informed about the proper procedure for dealing with patient complaints. And this is just one of a whole range of protocols and procedures you're supposed to know all about. Go through the list below, and mark each item with a tick or a cross to indicate whether you feel confident that you know enough about it. Be honest.

Do you know where your written complaints procedures are kept?	
Have you actually read them?	
Do you know who is responsible for handling complaints in your practice?	
Do you know all about information governance?	
Do you know all about health & safety / cleanliness & hygiene?	
Do you know about the QOF points system?	
Do you keep up to date with NICE guidelines for dealing with dementia, diagnosing hypertension, eating disorders, familial hypercholesterolaemia, etc.?	
Are you au fait with all the local patient care pathways which could save the NHS money by reducing referrals to the hospital?	

If it's not possible for any one person to be properly conversant with all these procedures and all this information, what's the answer?

- Do you have a system for trying to keep all this information somewhere so you can lay your hands on it if it's needed?

- Do you have one person in your surgery who acts as a 'librarian'?

- Do you go on update courses?

- Do you try to share out learning tasks within the practice team, and then update each other at regular meetings?

- Do you stick your head in the sand and hope it will all go away?

- Any other methods of coping?

When Tina leaves the surgery because Dr Hairy has insulted her new hairstyle, he's got no idea how he's going to cope. He doesn't know how the photocopier works or where the biscuits are kept. In your own surgery, how reliant are you on admin staff to keep things ticking over? How many admin tasks are you able to do if you have to? Again, put a tick or a cross, and be honest.

Can you book an appointment?	
Can you register a new patient?	
Can you replace the toner cartridge in your printer?	
Can you use the Choose and Book system?	
Can you scan a document?	

Are there any admin tasks you are particularly proud of knowing how to do, and are there any admin tasks you feel ashamed of not knowing how to do?

Dr Underslider has a special method of coping with difficult and irritating patients – he presses a buzzer, and a member of staff comes rushing in to tell him there's an emergency.

Have you ever engineered an 'interruption' to cut short a tricky consultation? Have you got any other tricks you use to get out of difficult situations? Crying? Faking a heart attack? Jumping out of the window? Pretending to be your own identical twin?

Dr Underslider also subjects Tina to sexual harassment when she goes to work for him.

Have you ever

- been subjected to sexual harassment yourself?

- had experience of any cases of sexual harassment?

- had experience of anyone being falsely accused of sexual harassment?

If you haven't had experience of any of the above, what do you think you'd do if you were in Tina's situation? If you're male, do you think it's possible for males to be sexually harassed?

EXERCISE: ✏ Your values as a doctor and a person

Dr Underslider clearly doesn't care very much about his patients – in fact he doesn't seem to care about anything much except getting what he wants. Dr Hairy is more idealistic but easily irritated by his patients, and finds it difficult to apply his ideals in real-life situations. What kind of doctor do you think you are, or what would you like to be? Try placing the following list of values in order of priority (by writing numbers next to them):

- Compassion
- Empathy
- Tolerance
- Job satisfaction
- Resilience (toughness?)
- Reflection
- Emotion
- Financial acumen
- Good organization
- Drive/ambition
- Ability to 'switch off' and relax
- Sense of duty
- Adrenaline
- A well-ordered life
- Sense of self-preservation
- Broadmindedness
- Firm opinions and views
- Ability to be analytical
- Equanimity
- Intellectual curiosity
- Intuitiveness
- Professional distance
- Approachability and accessibility
- Leadership
- Sense of humour
- Creativity

You can amend the list if you want to. Cross items off if you don't think they're relevant, and add items of your own if you think something important has been missed.

Now look at the list again.

- Do you think some list items are more important to your personal wellbeing than to your practice as a GP?

- Do you think your list reflects what you're actually like, or is it more an indication of what you aspire to?

- Is a bit of selfishness/insisting on time for yourself/wanting to have some fun always a bad thing?

POEM: 📖 The Last Words of My English Grandmother

There were some dirty plates
and a glass of milk
beside her on a small table
near the rank, disheveled bed—

Wrinkled and nearly blind
she lay and snored
rousing with anger in her tones
to cry for food,

Gimme something to eat—
They're starving me—
I'm all right I won't go
to the hospital. No, no, no

Give me something to eat
Let me take you
to the hospital, I said
and after you are well

you can do as you please.
She smiled, Yes
you do what you please first
then I can do what I please—

Oh, oh, oh! she cried
as the ambulance men lifted
her to the stretcher—
Is this what you call

making me comfortable?
By now her mind was clear—
Oh you think you're smart
you young people,

she said, but I'll tell you
you don't know anything.
Then we started.
On the way

we passed a long row
of elms. She looked at them
awhile out of
the ambulance window and said,

What are all those
fuzzy looking things out there?
Trees? Well, I'm tired
of them and rolled her head away.

WILLIAM CARLOS WILLIAMS

William Carlos Williams (1883–1963) was a GP himself. The poem presents us with a very clear-eyed and unsentimental view of illness and old age and infirmity. The old lady in the poem resents all the people who are trying to help her – 'they're starving me', she says; she complains about the ambulance men when they try to help her onto the stretcher; and she sneers at young people because they think they're smart. Is this representative of the way people behave in times of illness (or other stress)? Do they tend to relieve their feelings by lashing out at those around them, even those who are trying to help?

She is obviously living in very degraded circumstances – 'dirty plates', 'the rank, disheveled bed' and is 'wrinkled and nearly blind' – but she hasn't lost her willpower. 'I'm all right. I won't go to the hospital. No no no!' She comes across as angry and argumentative, but there are also glimpses of intelligence and humour – 'Yes, you do what you please first, then I can do what I please' and 'Is this what you call making me comfortable?'.

At the end of the poem, the arbitrariness of her declaration that she's tired of trees seems to indicate that actually she's tired of everything – tired of life itself.

Does this remind you of any experiences you've had yourself, either with patients or your own relatives? Do you have any other comments about the poem?

VIDEO: ▶ **Frank talking** (Part 3)

THEMES:

- Gossip

- Learning to live with difficult patients. Learning to accept that sometimes you just have to put up with them

- Coping with difficulties within the surgery team

- Relationships with other surgeries

- Relationships between GPs

- Different ways of being a GP – Dr Underslider just uses it as a means of getting the lifestyle he wants, and regards the patients as a nuisance to be outwitted in any way possible. Dr Hairy tries to deal with things more honestly, but often seems to end up on the receiving end

- Listening – how good is Dr Hairy at listening to Tina?

QUESTIONS ❓:

Answer at least one of the following:

- Have you ever jumped to a conclusion about somebody else which turned out to be false? (e.g. that they were overly fond of drink, having an affair, wearing a toupee?)

- Have you ever had somebody else jump to a conclusion about yourself which was false?

- Have you ever found out some startling fact about somebody, but felt obliged to keep it to yourself, and if so, why?

- Do you know any examples of people whose lives or careers have been badly damaged by gossip and rumours, either founded or unfounded?

Sexual harassment in the workplace is one thing, but having a full-blown relationship in the workplace can create huge problems too. Have you ever had experience of any of the following? (mark the list with ticks and crosses):

A workplace love affair		
A workplace extra-marital affair		
Husband and wife working together for the same organization		
Husband and wife trying to work together while their marriage is breaking up		
Relatives working together		
An employer who thinks it's a good idea to employ lots of people he or she knows socially		

Now mark the list again, this time with smiley faces or sad ones, to indicate whether things worked out all right or went badly wrong.

Is it better never to employ, or work with, people with whom you have a close personal relationship? If so, does this imply that you should try to keep your relationships with people at work professional, rather than allowing yourself to get too close to them on a personal level? Try to write a policy statement on this subject, to be included in a contract of employment.

How do you feel about working in a mixed-sex environment? Are single-sex teams better at getting things done? What are the characteristics of all-male teams? What are the characteristics of all-female teams?

Did you go to a mixed-sex school or a single-sex school, and how do you think this has influenced your relationships with members of the opposite sex in later life?

In a small community (or even a larger one) there can also be complications arising from your personal relationships with patients.

Answer one of the following questions:

Do you have personal friends amongst your patients, and if so do they expect special treatment, and do you actually treat them differently from your other patients? Is this something you've ever discussed amongst the practice team, and if so what were the results?

Have you ever had a relative as a patient, and if so what was the experience like?

Being a doctor, do you find yourself getting dragged into the medical care of your relatives, even though they're not registered with you, and how awkward does this make things between you and their own GP?

Gossip can be another very tricky area. Doctors are human beings, and human beings are fallible creatures. What with the stress of medical practice, it's nothing unusual for GPs to become involved in

- Marital difficulties
- Financial difficulties
- Depression and anxiety – perhaps even a breakdown
- Alcohol dependency
- Gambling addiction
- Drug addiction
- Fraud
- Hiring a Mafia hit-man
- Faking their own deaths
- Burning down their home or surgery for the insurance money

Have you had experience of any of these? (Mark the list with ticks or crosses.)

What was the reaction of the practice team? Were they supportive? Did they try to prevent the patients from finding out? If so, were they successful?

Answer one of the following:

- Have you ever known a GP whose reputation was ruined by some scandal, and who left general practice as a result?

- Have you ever known a GP who was struck off as the result of some scandal? If so, how did you feel about it? Did you think 'Serves the bugger right!' or 'There, but for the grace of God, go I'?

- GPs aren't immune from illness, of course, although in a funny way everybody tends to assume that they are. What examples have you come across of GPs experiencing the following, and how did the practice cope?:

  - Cancer

  - Stroke

  - Car accident

  - Other severe illness

- Were there contingency plans, or did the crisis reveal that everybody had just been hoping nothing would go wrong?

POEM: 📖 The Emperor of Ice-Cream

Call the roller of big cigars,
The muscular one, and bid him whip
In kitchen cups concupiscent curds.
Let the wenches dawdle in such dress
As they are used to wear, and let the boys
Bring flowers in last month's newspapers.
Let be be finale of seem.
The only emperor is the emperor of ice-cream.

Take from the dresser of deal,
Lacking the three glass knobs, that sheet
On which she embroidered fantails once
And spread it so as to cover her face.
If her horny feet protrude, they come
To show how cold she is, and dumb.
Let the lamp affix its beam.
The only emperor is the emperor of ice-cream.

WALLACE STEVENS

It can be quite difficult to make out what's going on in this poem until you've read it a few times. The clue is in the description of the sheet in the second part. A woman is lying dead, and a sheet which she embroidered herself is being used to cover her face. It's too short to cover all of her, and her feet stick out at the bottom.

The 'roller of big cigars', the 'wenches' and the boys who 'bring flowers in last month's newspapers' all seem to have come to help make arrangements for the funeral. Exactly what the 'roller of big cigars' is doing whipping up curds in a cup is unclear – some commentators think he's making ice-cream for the wake, because of the title of the poem, but others think he may be making some kind of preparation for embalming or beautifying the corpse.

The 'emperor of ice-cream' is death – the overlord of everything cold. So the line 'The only emperor is the emperor of ice-cream' is a way of saying 'the only thing that matters in the end is death', or perhaps 'the only thing that matters today (because of the dead woman and the funeral) is death'.

What does the line 'Let be be finale of seem' mean? Perhaps it means that when we're alive we spend all our time trying to *seem* – trying to make ourselves look good or important – but once we're dead we can only *be*.

The embroidered sheet seems to tell us a great deal about the dead woman's character. If you were lying dead, what one possession would you want placed with you to say something about your character, and why? Write this, and any other reactions to the poem, below.

VIDEO: ▶ 'Bramble jelly'

The 'Bramble Jelly' video shows Edward making jelly from blackberries, which is something he does every year.

- Do you have certain things you always do at the same time every year?

- Do you have any activities which make you feel more in touch with nature, or with the seasons, or both?

- How does it make you feel when things recur in a regular cycle, like blackberries ripening, the seasons changing, the stars moving around in the sky?

  - Does it give you a feeling of permanence, because those things are still happening just the same year after year, whatever else may change?

  - Does it give you a feeling of impermanence, because those things are still happening just the same while you get older, and will carry on happening after you're dead?

  - Do you worry that the pattern of the seasons is changing because of global warming?

  - Do you get all these feelings at the same time?

Making jelly from blackberries preserves them, but it also changes them. Bramble jelly doesn't taste the same as a fresh blackberry. In the same way, when we write about something which has happened, or when we look at a photograph of something which has happened, or even when we just remember something, what we have written, what is captured in the photograph or what we can remember is always slightly different from the original event.

When we reflect on an experience we fix the experience in our minds, but we also transform it. What is the nature of that transformation? Is it a good thing or a bad thing?

CHAPTER **8**

VIDEO: ▶ **Appraisal** (Part 1)

THEMES:

- Is the NHS user-friendly?
- Big issues and small issues in the GP's life
- How useful is the appraisal system? What's it for?
- Work–life balance

QUESTIONS ❓:

Answer one of the following:

- Write an account of the worst interview or exam you've ever had.

- Imagine you were an appraiser, appraising yourself. What would you say were your strengths and weaknesses? How do you think the strengths should be developed, and what should be done about the weaknesses?

- Imagine that on your next appraisal form you've got to tell one lie about something you've done or achieved. What would it be, and why?

In the video, the under-secretary recalls an occasion when his father attempted to tell him what it's like to be a GP, and he responded by asking for a tortoise.

Who do you talk to about what it feels like to be a GP? Are you married to another GP? Do you write things down in a diary? Or, instead of feeling a need to unburden yourself, do you just forget about work as soon as you're out of the surgery (and sometimes while you're still in it)?

If you ever talk to people outside the profession about your experiences, do they find it difficult to understand the GP's point of view? Do they tend to think you're terribly rich, when really you're terribly poor, for example; or are they astonished by your grumpiness and impatience with apparently ordinary and inoffensive people?

About the work–life balance: answer one of the following:

How do you retain a good work–life balance? Do you have non-medical hobbies or interests which you regard as essential to your sanity (for example membership of a secret society or collecting copies of the *Beano*)?

GPs (like the under-secretary's father) deal with life and death issues all the time – but does this give them a sense of perspective about ordinary life? In your experience, do they always see the big picture, or do they get just as wound up as anybody else about petty things? Do they lose it completely if they can't find their otoscopes, or if they run out of prescriptions just when they need to print one off? How would you rate your own behaviour in this respect? And is it sometimes important to involve yourself in the little things, in order to avoid being overwhelmed by the big ones?

About bureaucracy and technology in the NHS: answer at least one of the following:

Do you think the appraisal/revalidation system has been designed by a psychotic individual in the Department of Health with a personal grudge against the medical profession? If not, why not?

Can you describe any examples of people who have contemplated leaving the profession, or who have actually left, because of a new bureaucratic or technological requirement such as the online appraisal form or Choose & Book? Do you think this is generally more of a problem for older GPs than for younger ones?

Is the NHS user-friendly? Does it have the same incentive to make sure the end user's experience is a positive one as a market-driven company like Amazon? Does bad design in the NHS (the bad design of bureaucratic systems, and things like the online appraisal form) reflect

- an indifference to end users, or

- a failure of sympathy/imagination on the part of the designers, or just

- an absence of market forces?

If it's an absence of market forces, then does this imply that introducing market forces into the NHS would improve its efficiency and responsiveness to end users?

Can you think of any instances where the NHS's user-friendliness has improved in the last few years?

Dr Hairy doesn't really like using Dr Gladstone as a locum, and complains about him behind his back, but every time he sees him face-to-face he ends up behaving in a very placatory way and booking him for another session.

Do you ever find yourself in a similar position with any of your colleagues or patients, or do you know of an example of anybody who is victimized by someone else and can't seem to break out of the pattern? How do you think situations like this should be dealt with, or do you think we sometimes just have to put up with them?

EXERCISE: ✏ Mini-appraisal

Here are some questions about your learning plans and personal development.

What would you describe as your strong point?

- Motivation

- Self-confidence

- Life experience

If it's motivation, what motivates you? If it's self-confidence, what are you self-confident about? Are there any areas where you feel less confident? If it's life experience, is this really just a way of trying to make a virtue out of your extreme old age?

Learning cycle:

- Name one new and important thing you've learned in the past year

- Name something you'd like to learn more about in the coming year

- Name something you used to know a lot about, but now most of it's gone

- Name something you've never known anything about, and which really bores you to tears, but other GPs keep going on about it as if it was important.

Which word applies best to yourself and your place of work at the moment?

- Transition (or reconfiguration)
- Consolidation
- Innovation

Can you explain why?

How would you describe yourself as a practitioner and a teacher/learner?

- Novice
- Advanced beginner
- Competent
- Proficient
- Expert

Can you explain why?

Do you think you're getting better as a GP, or worse? Do you feel that the job's getting tougher, or easier? When you see other GPs considerably older or considerably younger than yourself, do you think 'Ooh, I wish I could be more like that' or 'What a git'? (Be honest.)

POEM: 📖 The Poet Sings of the Wide North Sea

The moving mind that God gave me
is manifold as the wide North Sea
and as the sea is full of things,
the great fish in their wanderings
and the spread galleys of the old Kings
and darkness eddying round in rings,
so, packed with all that I have done
and felt and known and lost and won,
by the tide drifted and the wind inclined
moves my not measurable mind.

HILAIRE BELLOC

How does this poem reflect on the appraisal process? Is Belloc saying that it's really impossible to make a judgement about another person, because you can't fully know what's going on inside them? Or is he just suffering from water on the brain?

How good a description do you think this is of the different things people have going on in their heads?

Any other reactions to the poem?

CHAPTER **9**

VIDEO: ▶ Appraisal (Part 2)

THEMES:

- Difficulties with technology and bureaucracy (again)

- Gaming the system. Can the appraisal system be scammed? What other examples are there of scamming or gaming the system? To what extent is this a consequence of the way the system is designed? The differences between what is claimed in annual assessments (like the appraisal process) and what actually happens in everyday life

- Why do people become GPs?

QUESTIONS ❓:

Dr Hairy is having terrible difficulty filling in his appraisal form, and after he's been struggling with it he accidentally clicks the wrong thing and closes it without saving his work.

Describe the worst disaster you've ever had with a piece of digital technology.

Are you one of those people who say, 'Computers hate me', and do you feel convinced that you've only got to look at a piece of complicated technology for it to go wrong – or do you generally feel quite comfortable in the digital age? Give yourself a mark between 0 and 10, where 0 is blithering incompetence and 10 is supergeek status.

Is there somebody else who makes you feel woefully inadequate when it comes to dealing with technology, e.g. your partner, your son or daughter, or somebody you work with? What score between 0 and 10 would you give that other person?

When Dr Underslider hears that Dr Hairy is having difficulty with a form, he starts trying to guess which form it might be – an insurance report form, a SmartCard application form, and so on.

Here is a list of irritating forms. Write numbers next to them, to rank them in terms of their irritatingness. If you've never had to deal with one of them, just cross it through and count your blessings. If you can think of irritating forms of your own, which aren't on the list, feel free to add them.

SmartCard application form
Passport application form
Medical insurance report form
HGV licence examination form
Any job application form
The online appraisal form
If you're a registrar, the e-portfolio
DS1500 – Disability Living Allowance form
Blue Badge form for disabled parking
Any other suggestions?

What's so particularly irritating about the form you've placed at number one on your list? In general, would you rather fill out a form by hand or electronically? Is there any such thing as a well-designed form, can you give an example, and can you explain what's good about it?

Dr Underslider attaches all his Christmas cards to his appraisal form and calls them 'patient testimonials'. Answer at least one of the following questions:

- Do you get Christmas cards from the patients, or other testimonials? What do you do with them? Do you keep them in a special file, and do you ever attach them to your appraisal?

- Do you have patients who always give you a Christmas present, and if so do you regard the present as thanks for the work you've done during the year, or a way of trying to 'butter you up' for the year to come?

- Do you ever get Christmas presents from patients you don't like, and if so, does it make you nicer to them next time you see them?

- What kinds of Christmas presents would you share with other people at the surgery, and what kinds would you keep to yourself?

Dr Underslider gets through his appraisals by telling great big fibs about what he does, instead of trying to change his working practice and then putting down the truth about this on his form.

Which is easier, the fibbing method or the honest one? Given the constraints on a GP's time, does the appraisal system actually have the effect of encouraging people to fib, rather than encouraging them to improve their practice?

Is there any alternative method of evaluation which would actually encourage people to improve practice instead of just saying they'd improved it? If so, what? *(This is a difficult question, so if you come up with anything particularly brilliant you'd probably better send it to your local Deanery.)*

Dr Hairy's appraisal form brings him to a halt by asking him lots of questions about clinical governance. What do you think his problem is?

- He just hasn't done any clinical governance, and hasn't even got a clue what it means

- He's done it, but he hasn't got any evidence that he's done it

- He's done it, but he hasn't got any written policies, procedures or contingency plans.

How commonplace is it for people working in the NHS to be caught out by being asked to produce written evidence of something they've been doing but not recording? Is the answer to always record everything, and always have written policies and procedures for everything you do? If this really is the answer, how much slower and more frustrating does it make your work?

EXERCISE:  Things you were told as a child / things you say to your children / sayings you live by

This exercise is about formative influences. It's also about the difference between aspiration and how things actually turn out.

When you were a child your parents probably said things to you like 'Sit up straight and don't fidget', 'Don't interrupt me when I'm talking on the phone', 'Don't slam the doors', 'You can't have any pudding until you've finished what's on the plate', 'You'll get square eyes if you watch too much television', 'If you sit on that toilet too long you'll give yourself piles', 'Don't keep leaning back on that chair, you're going to break the back of it', etc. In the space below, write down the phrases you used to hear most often when you were little.

Look at the list again. Do you ever find yourself repeating the same phrases to your own kids? Or, if you don't have kids of your own, are there any phrases which used to be drummed into you when you were a child, and which didn't make any sense to you at the time, but they're starting to make a bit more sense now?

Now write down

- any pearls of wisdom you would like to pass on to your own children, such as 'The best things in life are free' or 'Do unto others as you would be done by', and/or

- any pieces of wisdom, sayings or quotations which you think have helped to shape your life, such as 'This above all, to thine own self be true', 'I must create my own system, or be enslaved by another man's', 'Go to the ant, thou sluggard; consider her ways, and be wise', or 'One thing I can tell you is you've got to be free'.

If appropriate, and if you can remember where they come from, give attributions for these sayings – Shakespeare, William Blake, the Book of Proverbs, John Lennon, etc.

While we're soul-searching, answer at least one of the following questions:

- Why did you decide to become a GP? Who was the person, or who were the people, who had the greatest influence on your choice of career?

- If you could change one thing about the way you deal with patients and/or colleagues, what would it be and why?

- What's the nicest letter, present, or other sign of appreciation you've ever had from a patient?

VIDEO: ▶ 'Everyone I can think of who has died'

The 'Everyone I can think of who has died' video shows Edward Picot writing onto leaves all the names he could call to mind of people who had meant something to him and who had died. The list included relatives, pets, friends, patients from the surgery where he works, and famous people – but the rule was they had to have meant something to him personally. Once he'd written their names onto the leaves, he floated the leaves down a stream near to his house.

Spend five minutes writing down on a separate piece of paper the names of people who have died who were important to you.

- Have you written the name of a famous person, and if so why?
- Have you written the name of a friend or relative, and if so why?
- Have you written the name of a patient, and if so why?

Why does it seem appropriate to write people's names onto leaves, and float them down a stream? How does this compare to putting someone's name onto a plaque, for example, or a tombstone?

CHAPTER **10**

VIDEO: ▶ **Appraisal** (Part 3)

THEMES:

- How some GPs become inseparable from their jobs
- Coping with role reversal/loss of control
- Coping with criticism
- Lifelong learning/professional development

QUESTIONS ❓:

In consultations with their patients, GPs are normally the ones in control, while their patients are the ones feeling nervous and hoping that things are going to turn out all right. In an appraisal, the boot is on the other foot.

- Do you think one of the attractive things about being a GP is this sense of being in control, having the power to help people or withhold help from them, which in many cases means that they will look up to you as a sort of superior being?

- Do you think it's good for GPs to be on the receiving end once in a while?

- When was the last time you went to see a GP or consultant yourself? How did it make you feel? Do you think you were treated differently because of being a doctor?

Do you have any little tricks for putting your patients more at ease and making them feel that you're on the same level as them?

Do you sit on the other side of the desk from the patient, or on the same side?	
What's the first thing you normally say when a patient comes into your room?	
Can the patient see the computer screen just as well as you can see it yourself?	
When you're doing things on the computer, do you always try to explain what you're doing?	
If you were going to take a blood pressure reading, would you explain why you were doing it before, during or after?	

Are there occasions when, instead of treating the consultation as a partnership between equals, you need to take back control – for example if a patient is rambling off the point, if you are dealing with badly-behaved children, or if the patient's demands are unreasonable? If so, what do you do?

Have you ever felt intimidated or threatened by a patient? If so, why, and how did you cope?

Have you got an alarm button of some kind in your consulting room?

How much difference do you think it makes whether you're male or female?

Imagine that you have an appraisal where the appraiser has to say something you don't want to hear – pointing out an apparent gap in your learning, for example, or bringing up something bad that came out of your 360-degree feedback.

Below are some typical reactions to criticism and accusations. It's common for people to feel all of these in a mixture, but for some people one feeling dominates, and for other people it's another. Write numbers next to the responses to indicate which ones seem to be most dominant in your own case, and which are least.

Guilt and submissiveness: a feeling that you must be in the wrong, and that the person accusing or criticizing you must be right: an impulse to resolve the situation by immediately taking some kind of corrective action or making some kind of atonement. 'Yes, you're absolutely right, I'm really sorry and I'll try to make sure that it never happens again. I'll write a letter of apology.'

Resentment/defensiveness: a feeling that you've been wronged, a feeling that you're being 'got at' (probably for personal reasons), a feeling that it's 'not fair', a desire to be exonerated, an impulse to lash out, and a wish to see the people accusing or criticizing you punished for their actions. 'I know who's behind this. You haven't heard the last of this. I'm going straight to my solicitor.'

Disorientation and flight: you don't recognize this version of events or this way of looking at things, and you can't understand the mindset of anyone who could see things in this way. An impulse to withdraw from the conflict and be on your own, to 'lick your wounds' in private, to go away and do something entirely different. 'Oh, well, if that's how people feel then I might as well just pack it in. I never really liked it here anyway.'

Claiming ownership: a desire to regain control of the situation as quickly as possible by declaring that you already knew about the problems and you were already doing something about them. 'Yes, yes, I know, I'm already aware of this and I've already got it in hand.'

'Let's get it over with': a feeling that you don't care what happens next, as long as it's over and done with quickly, so that you don't have to think about it any more and you can get on with the rest of your life. 'Yes, all right, do whatever you like, I don't care, just send me a letter; I'm too busy to cope with this now.'

Delaying tactics: a feeling that the whole problem may just go away if you can stick your head in the sand and ignore it for long enough. 'I'll deal with this next week/next month/next year/after I get back from my holiday/after I retire/after I'm dead.'

Any other typical reactions you can think of?

Putting the boot back on the other foot – you saying something unwelcome to a patient, instead of somebody else saying something unwelcome to you - do you have any techniques for broaching unpleasant subjects? For example, telling people that

- they're overweight

- they've got raised blood pressure

- they've got CKD

- they've got diabetes

- they've got heart failure

- they've got one of the cancers.

Do you ever try, for example, to use a good news/bad news/good news sandwich? ('Well, there's no sign of any cancer. But I'm afraid we've discovered something else – you've got diabetes. But now we know what the problem is, we should be able to do something about it, and help you to feel a bit better.') Or telling them the worst possible scenario first, so that everything that comes afterwards seems like a comparative relief?

Do you ever find yourself not telling the patient something because you feel that the patient won't be able to accept it? For example, if you told a patient he/she was diabetic, and the information got a really bad reaction, would you go ahead and tell the patient that he/she had CKD as well?

EXERCISE: ✏ Breaking bad news to the tennis player

Pretend you're a knee surgeon who has been consulted by the best tennis player in the world, and your investigations have revealed that there is a fundamental problem with the knee which is going to put an end to the player's career in tennis. How are you going to break it to him?

What would your opening sentence be?

Would you have an ideal end to the consultation in mind, and try to work towards it? For example, trying to get him to think about things like coaching and commentary, so that you can part company on a slightly more positive note?

At the same time, how do you avoid making light of his real disappointment, and what advice will you give him about how to deal with the emotional aspect of things?

CHAPTER **11**

VIDEO: ▶ Appraisal (Part 4)

THEMES:

- The influence of your upbringing on your adult life
- The influence of your job on your character and sense of self
- Lifelong learning
- Leadership (again)

QUESTIONS ❓:

Dr Stead says he's been trying to get out from under people like Dr Gladstone all his life: clearly his boyhood experiences have made a lasting impression on his personality and his aims in life. Similarly, the under-secretary's childhood difficulties with his father have had a lasting influence on him, and through him a lasting influence on the NHS.

Answer at least one of the following:

- Give an example of a patient whose whole life seems to have been soured by his or her upbringing

- On the other hand, give an example of a patient (or anybody else you know) whose upbringing seems to have had a very positive effect – made them very self-confident, given them a very strong work ethic, a very strong sense of values, etc.

- Even if you didn't enjoy your upbringing, is the struggle to escape from the circumstances of your childhood sometimes a positive thing? Can you give an example of this?

- Where would you place yourself on this spectrum? Has your upbringing had a good influence on you, a bad influence, or a mixture of the two? Have you tried to escape from it, or to live up to it?

In the video, Dr Gladstone pleads with Dr Stead not to take away his stethoscope, because he says being a doctor is the reason people respect him and the thing that gives him his identity – 'It's what makes me me. If you stop me from being a doctor I'll just be a fat old chap who likes cakes.'

Is this how you feel about being a doctor, or could you give it up without a qualm? If there are particular things you would miss about it, and particular things which you would really like to be rid of, say what they are.

Do you think doctoring is unique because of the way it shapes the identities of the people who practise it, or do you think there are other professions which have a similar effect?

What are your experiences of GPs who have retired, or been forced to give up the job for some reason? How have they coped?

How long do you intend to keep working as a doctor? Do you have any plans for what you intend to do with your life after you stop?

Dr Hairy says that a good GP should have a commitment to lifelong learning. Apart from attending professional development meetings, do you use any other methods of 'blowing away the cobwebs' and keeping up to date? Put ticks next to the items on the list below which apply to you:

- Do you go on training courses?
- Do you do any online learning?
- Is clinical guidance included with your clinical system, and if so do you ever use it?
- What about reading books?
- Do you read medical magazines such as the *BMJ* or the *Lancet*?
- Do you read NICE guidelines? What was the last one you read?
- Do you learn from other GPs? Do you and other GPs ever have get-togethers where you share your learning with each other?
- Any other learning method you use?

What's your preferred learning method?

- Learning by yourself
- Sharing information in a group
- Attending a seminar or lecture
- Other

(Put numbers next to the list items to rank them in order of preference.)

Leadership again:

Dr Underslider ends up in charge of a professional development group, not because he's a particularly suitable person for the job but because he's got the gift of the gab. Dr Gladstone ends up facilitating the group, again not because he's particularly suitable but because he's looking for an alternative to locum work. In the NHS, and in plenty of other places, the people who end up in positions of responsibility are quite often not there because they're more capable than anybody else, but because

- they're prepared to put themselves forward
- they're prepared to put up with the hassle the job involves
- they know the people who were choosing the candidates
- they've got the right kind of background/accent/face, and
- lots of quite capable people were too apathetic to apply.

In terms of getting involved and helping to run things, rank the following statements by writing numbers next to them, to indicate which applies to you the most, and which the least:

I sit on lots of committees and I think it's very important to get involved. I'm always prepared to volunteer. I can't stand these people who are always ready to criticize but can't be bothered to make an effort or come up with a better idea themselves. Also, I like to feel important, I love the sound of my own voice, and frankly I'd rather sit in a committee room drinking coffee all morning than have to see all those bloody stupid patients.

I'd love to get more involved but I'm just too busy. How can people find the time for all this committee work? I'm at the surgery until seven o'clock in the evening looking at blood test results and writing referral letters. Then when I get home I have to help the kids with their homework. Where did my life go? How come I never get any me time any more?

The people who sit on these committees all know each other, and they've made up their minds how they want to run things, and the last thing they want is some interloper barging in and telling them they're doing everything wrong. They wouldn't listen anyway. I've got loads of ideas, really good ones, but people like that don't want to listen to good ideas. They just want to sit round agreeing with each other all day long. We should kill the lot of them and start all over again.

What's the point of getting involved? The whole thing's a scam. This Government's hell-bent on dismantling the NHS, and if you get involved with all these commissioning groups you're just playing into their hands. They know perfectly well that these reforms won't work. They actually want it to fail, so they can bring in more private provision. The government are in the hands of the multinationals, the multinationals are in the hands of the Mafia, and the Mafia's run by Martians.

What do you dream about?

At the end of the video, Dr Stead has a dream about his mother, some bees, his trousers, the Mighty Buffalo and the appraisal system, all muddled up together.

What was the last dream you had that you can remember? Was it a nice dream or a nasty dream? Did it take you back into the past, or was it about the here-and-now, or a mixture of both? Was it about work? If it was an anxiety dream, what were you anxious about? Was it in colour or black and white?

EXERCISE: ⊘ Learning into teaching /
Marcus Aurelius

The quotations below are all taken from the *Meditations* of the Roman emperor Marcus Aurelius. Marcus Aurelius was a famous disciple of Stoic philosophy.

'... resolve firmly... to do what comes to hand with correct and natural dignity, and with humanity, independence, and justice.'

'Our mental powers should enable us to perceive the swiftness with which all things vanish away: their bodies in the world of space, and their remembrance in the world of time.'

'You will never be remarkable for quick-wittedness... Cultivate these, then, for they are wholly within your power; sincerity, for example, and dignity; industriousness, and sobriety. Avoid grumbling; be frugal, considerate, and frank; be temperate in manner and in speech.'

'As for truth, it is so veiled in obscurity that many reputable philosophers assert the impossibility of reaching any certain knowledge... all our intellectual conclusions are fallible; for where is the infallible man?'

'Accustom yourself to give careful attention to what others are saying, and try your best to enter into the mind of the speaker.'

'Is it possible for any useful thing to be achieved without change? Do you not see, then, that change in yourself is of the same order, and no less necessary...'

'Your own mind, the mind of the universe, your neighbour's mind – be prompt to explore them all.'

'Waste no more time arguing what a good man should be. Be one.'

'What are the children of men, but as leaves that drop at the wind's breath?'

'What is your trade? Goodness. But how are you to make a success of it unless you have a philosopher's insight into the nature of the universe, and into the particular constitution of man?'

'Practice, even when success looks hopeless. The left hand, inept in other respects for lack of practice, can grasp the reins more firmly than the right, because here it has had practice.'

'If it is not the right thing to do, never do it; if it is not the truth, never say it. Keep your impulses in hand.'

'But I have played no more than three of the five acts.' Just so; in your drama of life, three acts are all the play... Pass on your way, then, with a smiling face...'

These are very admirable and high-minded sentiments, but they may be difficult to apply in everyday life.

Think about Dr Underslider. He doesn't seem to have any principles of the kind Marcus Aurelius goes on about; instead he has lots of tricks for getting what he wants out of particular situations. You could think of different ways of dealing with life's difficulties as a spectrum, with Dr Underslider's tricks at one end, and Marcus Aurelius' highly ethical approach at the other. Dr Underslider's approach is very practical, but selfish and short-term in its aims. Marcus Aurelius' sayings are values-based and good for keeping things in perspective, but may be difficult to apply to the complexities of everyday life.

- Which end of the spectrum do you think you find yourself on the most?

- Do you think different approaches are suitable for different situations? For example, do you think tricks are all right for dealing with irritating and trivial situations, whereas the more principled approach is suitable for dealing with big serious issues? What would happen if you tried it the other way round?

POEM: 📖 On the Death of Dr Robert Levet

Condemn'd to hope's delusive mine,
As on we toil from day to day,
By sudden blasts, or slow decline,
Our social comforts drop away.

Well tried through many a varying year,
See Levet to the grave descend;
Officious, innocent, sincere,
Of ev'ry friendless name the friend.

Yet still he fills affection's eye,
Obscurely wise, and coarsely kind;
Nor, letter'd arrogance, deny
Thy praise to merit unrefin'd.

When fainting nature call'd for aid,
And hov'ring death prepar'd the blow,
His vig'rous remedy display'd
The power of art without the show.

In misery's darkest caverns known,
His useful care was ever nigh,
Where hopeless anguish pour'd his groan,
And lonely want retir'd to die.

No summons mock'd by chill delay,
No petty gain disdain'd by pride,
The modest wants of ev'ry day
The toil of ev'ry day supplied.

His virtues walk'd their narrow round,
Nor made a pause, nor left a void;
And sure th' Eternal Master found
The single talent well employ'd.

The busy day, the peaceful night,
Unfelt, uncounted, glided by;
His frame was firm, his powers were bright,
Tho' now his eightieth year was nigh.

Then with no throbbing fiery pain,
No cold gradations of decay,
Death broke at once the vital chain,
And free'd his soul the nearest way.

SAMUEL JOHNSON

This poem was written shortly before Johnson's death.

What do you think of Dr Levet and what does Johnson highlight about him that makes him a good doctor? Do you recognize any of the virtues from the Marcus Aurelius quotes in this poem?

POEM: 📖 This is Just to Say

I have eaten
the plums
that were in
the icebox

and which
you were probably
saving
for breakfast

Forgive me
they were delicious
so sweet
and so cold

WILLIAM CARLOS WILLIAMS

Williams was an actual GP (and famous modernist poet) who lived in the USA. His poem isn't about duty or being conscientious; it's about living for the moment. One person has put plums in the fridge to keep them fresh, but to the writer of the poem this has only served to make them more delicious, and he therefore steals them. The note-form of the poem is meant to be appropriate to the impulsive, unpremeditated way he has acted.

Who do you feel sympathy with, the person who put the plums in the fridge, or the person who stole them? How important is it to live 'in the moment', enjoying the intensity of your sensations, and how difficult is it to do this when you're leading the busy, duty-driven life of a GP?

Which of the two poems do you like the best, and why? ('I like the second one because it's shorter' is a perfectly acceptable answer.)

An extra page for you to continue your poetry appreciation:

CHAPTER **12**

VIDEO: ▶ **Child safety**

THEMES:

- Child safety isn't always about cases of sexual abuse; it can be about neglect, or about the child being brought up in a violent environment

- The people and families involved in these issues aren't always the ones you might expect

- The perpetrators of domestic violence don't always see themselves as bad people – which makes them harder to spot

QUESTIONS ❓:

Answer one of the following:

Write an account of an actual safeguarding case that you have been involved in or that you know about. Do you think it could have been handled better, and if so, how?

Dr Gladstone says 'you should never interfere between a man and his wife', and some GPs may feel strongly that it's not their job to investigate the private lives of their patients or pass moral judgements.

- How do you feel about this?

- Is there a point at which the safety of the child should become the overriding consideration? If so, when is that point?

Dr Underslider suggests referring the case to Social Services or the police. Are these the only two agencies to which the case could be taken, or can you think of any others?

Dr Hairy talks to Tina because she knows Mr Greengrow personally and he wants to see if he can get any corroborative evidence about what's going on in Mr Greengrow's household. Dr Underslider, in his own inappropriate style, suggests that the way forward is to get corroborative evidence by investigating the matter further.

- Is it appropriate to discuss confidential matters like this with other members of the practice team?

- If the wife was registered with another GP, would it be appropriate to ask the other GP what they knew about her, and if they'd seen any evidence of wife-beating?

- What about asking the son's school?

- Any other thoughts about how the case could be investigated further?

In the end, Dr Hairy isn't sure whether he's got enough evidence to take action – he doesn't want to make any accusations against Mr Greengrow in case they aren't true – and he also isn't sure about the proper procedure, so he does nothing at all.

Do you think this ever happens in real life when GPs are faced with cases of this sort, but unsure of their ground? Have you ever found yourself in a similar situation?

Dr Gladstone has some harsh things to say about Social Services:

- Any time you want them to help you, they just give you a lot of excuses

- They're not properly trained or qualified like doctors

In your own surgery, what's the liaison with Social Services like? Do they ever come to meetings? Do you know how to contact them? When was the last time you tried, and did you find them helpful or unhelpful?

Mr Greengrow has apparently bought himself a bride off the internet.

- If the bride is underage or has been married against her will, is this automatically an offence? What if she comes from a culture in which arranged marriages and underage marriages are normal practice?

- What if she isn't underage and there's no evidence of coercion? Is buying a bride off the internet still an offence?

- How important are cultural norms in determining the rightness or wrongness of particular actions? In Shakespeare's play Romeo and Juliet, Juliet was under fourteen years old, yet Shakespeare doesn't seem to disapprove of her having sex with Romeo. Does this mean that Romeo and Juliet is a paedophile play?

POEM: 📖 Wifebeating

What I would like to say about wifebeating is
I have no first-hand knowledge
really, no broken bones or loosened teeth.
The bruises faded and I do not let him in the apartment anymore.

I have not been beaten because while
smashing me against the wall, he said
he was not doing anything I did not deserve
and I wasn't sure that he was wrong
and three men in the apartment
closed the door so they would not see
it not happen.

But I hear my child's screams in the night.
He demands her presence,
says he does it in front of her
to show her what kind of mother I am.

I am not the type of person who gets beaten. I
am nice and intelligent and a doctor, and he is not
a wifebeater because he is a minister, so it is impossible
I was assaulted.

I know I cannot have been beaten, each time worse than
before, because I have asked for help many times,
asked men, because he does not like women anymore,
asked for someone to say:
What are you doing? It is not right
to threaten your wife...

Instead they ask me what I did to justify his rage
And they have each done
Nothing. Therefore, these fights cannot
be happening, and I do not believe them
anymore.

Besides, it does not happen very often,
I have learned to keep my mouth shut.
I have left the house, abandoned my child's
fishtank and Christmas decorations.
He says I have abandoned him, his grieving friends approach
about my desertion, his broken heart...
and I am shamed.

But you asked about wife beating and I am not the one
to talk about it, as you can see. Because I have not
been threatened with murder which happened to a friend
of mine whose husband stabbed her

twenty-six times
in front of their three kids
and no one came 'til
she was dead.

It must have taken a long time to stick in the knife
and take it out and stick it in again
twenty-six times
in front of the kids to show them
what kind of a mother they had.

MARTHA DEED

POEM: 📖 Red Suspenders

The evil man in red suspenders told his son to be home
by 11:30. When the boy had not appeared by 11:35
the man ripped his mohair overcoat – the tan one
not the gray – from its red cedar hanger in the front
hall closet. Then he ran down the street to the party,
grabbed his son by the scruff of the neck,
interrupting teenage laughter, and dragged him
home – his son's shoes clattering and skippering
on the pavement as he tried to match his father's stride.
Once inside, the man beat his son until he was tired.
The evil man told this story on himself
at a trial recess in a courtroom
filled with people
unsympathetic to his client.
His words bounced off the walls.
He said children must learn to obey
from an early age. He held his side
as he spoke. He'd broken three ribs
the night before when his car went off the road.
"I wasn't wearing a seatbelt," he said.
"No one tells me what to do."

MARTHA DEED

Martha Deed is a writer from the USA, who for thirty years worked as a psychologist specializing in family law issues – often cases of domestic violence. Both these poems are from her 2010 collection *The Lost Shoe* (http://chapbookpublisher.com/shop.html).

Do the two men in these poems think they are in the wrong or in the right? What about the woman in the first poem? She says her husband told her 'he was not doing anything I did not deserve, and I wasn't sure that he was wrong'.

How common is it for the victims of violence to blame themselves for what's happening?

The man in the first poem is a minister, and his wife is a doctor. In the second poem, the man has 'a client' and tells his story 'at a trial recess in a courtroom' – so we gather that he must be a lawyer. These are well-educated and well-to-do people; not the kind we would expect to be involved in domestic violence. Is this something that could only happen in the USA, or could it happen here too?

Any other reactions to these poems? Do you like them, or would you prefer to read something less harrowing?

EXTRA VIDEO: ▶ 'Dr Hairy in: Mentoring'

The theme of child protection is a slightly grim one on which to end the book, so a look at the 'Dr Hairy in: Mentoring' video can be a nice way to cheer yourself up again. It can also serve as a means of reaffirming and summing up the values and methods of the book as a whole.

In the video, Dr Hairy decides to get himself a mentor because he's completely at the end of his tether and doesn't know where to turn. This makes the mentoring system sound a bit like a Samaritans for GPs, which isn't exactly the case; GPs very often seek out mentors when they feel that their careers are in crisis, but the mentoring system can also be useful when doctors just want help making a decision about which direction they should go in, or sometimes just when they feel the need of someone else to talk things over with.

The video does make a couple of points about mentoring which are worth reinforcing, however:

- The mentor often gets just as much out of the process as the mentee

- There should be mentoring available in all areas of the UK, organized by the local Deanery

- Mentoring isn't about one person telling another person what to think – it's about trying to help people to reflect and get an overview – and in that sense it's very similar to what this book tries to achieve

Dr Ye, the mentor in the video, doesn't solve Dr Hairy's problems for him and he doesn't tell him what to do. In fact he doesn't talk to him directly about his difficulties at all. Nevertheless he makes Dr Hairy feel much better. How does he achieve this, and does he do it on purpose or by accident? Is the sense of perspective coming out of Dr Ye, or is it actually coming out of Dr Hairy?

Some of Dr Ye's 'Poetic Sayings' are real quotations, and some of them are just made up. See how many of the sayings you can remember, whether you can spot which ones are real and which ones are invented, and then decide which ones you like the most. There's a crib-sheet below.

Dr Ye's sayings:

- How does an image of the sun get into the heart of a flower? How does the sound of the sea get into an empty shell? *(invented)*

- The journey itself is your destination *(genuine – from Basho, the famous Japanese Zen Haiku poet)*

- The moon is brighter since the barn burnt down *(genuine – another one from Basho)*

- The poppy is like a girl's heart, and the snail is like her ear *(invented)*
- The cut worm blesses the plough *(genuine – from William Blake, the mystical English poet)*
- The best pig farmer is a great big sausage *(invented)*
- When you paint a wall, is it the wall that's being painted, or is the wall painting you? *(invented)*